# EXPLORING BIOLOGY

General Biology Laboratory Activities

SECOND EDITION

San Diego Mesa College Biology Faculty and Staff
Illustrated by Alicia Ann Hall

RandomNPC LLC Carlsbad, CA USA

*Potentially useful information for your many adventures.*

Exploring Biology: General Biology Laboratory Activities
Authors: Janice Clymer, Anita Plagge, Tim Plagge, Matt Fay
Illustrated by Alicia Ann Hall
ISBN 978-0-9883737-3-0

Additional illustrations by Matt Fay
Photos by Tim Plagge and Janice Clymer

## Dedication

This lab manual is dedicated to the biology students at San Diego Mesa College. It is our pleasure and honor to spend time with you on your life's journey. You inspire, delight, and challenge us. These activities are intended to help you explore the wonders of life.

—The authors

# TABLE OF CONTENTS

# INTRODUCTION TO THE BIOLOGY LABORATORY

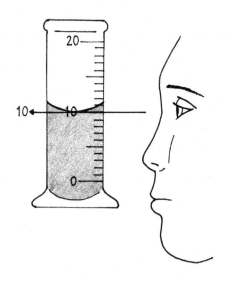

What do you do in a biology laboratory? A biology laboratory (lab) is one place where you can study life under controlled conditions. You are probably aware that biologists, like all scientists, may do some sort of experimentation in a lab. What kind of experiments can be done to study life? What equipment or materials are needed? Is it dangerous? Are there hazards that are specific to studying biology? How do biologists decide what, exactly, they are to do in the lab? How do they collect information from their experiments? How is that information gathered, organized and communicated? These questions will form the framework for your activities in today's lab.

In the first part of today's lab, your instructor will discuss the layout of the laboratory and how to safely conduct experiments. Then you will learn the appropriate methods of studying science. Crucial to your studies this semester will be becoming proficient at measuring techniques and being able to construct and design experiments as well as communicate your results. Today in lab you will become familiar with both measuring techniques and experimental design. You will conduct a simple experiment and summarize your results to communicate them both graphically and verbally.

**STUDENT LEARNING OUTCOMES**

Upon completion of today's lab, you will be able to do the following:

I.   discuss the layout of the laboratory and laboratory safety procedures,
II.  describe the steps of the scientific method,
III. use equipment to measure volume, mass, length, and temperature in metric units,
IV.  design an experiment, and
V.   graph and communicate experimental results.

## I. LABORATORY SAFETY

**Procedure**

STEP 1. Listen as your instructor describes the room layout, key safety equipment, and safe practices for the laboratory.

STEP 2. Determine the location of the fire extinguisher, safety showers and eye washes. The safety data sheet (SDS) for chemicals used in this laboratory are available. If you have any questions about the use of safety equipment, ask your instructor.

1. Where is the first aid kit? *- lab Cabinet*

2. Where is the broken glass container? *by skeleton, whiteboard.*

3. Where is the fire extinguisher? *by the fumehood*

No food or drink is permitted in the lab. Wear sensible clothes, including closed-toe shoes in consideration of the fact that you will be using harsh chemicals, sharp instruments, and biohazards. Wear gloves for dissections and avoid touching your face or eyes during lab without washing your hands first. Do not wear loose clothing, and tie your hair back if necessary when using a flame, hot plate, or spinning equipment; do not lean or reach over an open flame. Report any damaged equipment such as frayed electrical cords. If you have any questions about the use of equipment, ask your instructor. **Wash your hands at the end of each lab.**

4. What adjustments to your attire do you need to make for lab? *Closed toe Shoes, non flowing clothes, no strappy clothes*

If you break glass or equipment, notify those around you and the instructor, and clean up with a brush and dustpan. Broken glass goes in the cardboard glass container. *If you are injured, notify the instructor immediately so that proper medical attention can be obtained.*

5. What do you do in case of glass breakage? *tell the teacher.*

6. What do you do in case of an injury?

*tell the teacher*

## GENERAL RULES FOR THE BIOLOGY LABORATORY

1. Never eat food or drink beverages in the lab; food and drink may not be on the bench tops.
2. Always wear closed-toe shoes in the lab.
3. Wear proper laboratory attire at all times and personal protective equipment when instructed to do so.
4. Know the location and the proper use of laboratory safety equipment, including:

    emergency call box/button,
    fire extinguisher,
    shower and eyewash stations,
    fume hood,
    first aid kit,
    gas shut off,
    spill kit.
5. Know your evacuation route, in case of emergency.
6. Know the materials you will be using in lab and understand how to handle them in a proper and safe manner.
7. Know the type of waste you are generating in lab and only dispose of it in the approved manner.
8. Make sure all items are clean and returned to their proper location at the end of the lab period.
9. Clean your laboratory area by wiping down the bench top at the end of each lab period.

Write any additional rules provided by your lab instructor here.

STEP 3. Please read the following statement, then on the next page, sign and date it, print your name, and enter your lab CRN. Tear out and give the completed and signed sheet to your lab instructor. A copy of the statement is included here for your future reference.

I am familiar with the layout of the Biology 107 lab, available safety equipment, and good safety practices for the lab. I have read and will comply with the General Rules of the Lab. I accept responsibility for compliance with safety practices and rules. I understand that failure to follow good practices and the general rules of the lab may result in injury and I accept full responsibility for any injury that may result if I do not comply with them and will be dismissed from lab.

## II. THE SCIENTIFIC METHOD

### II. A. The scientific method described

**Procedure**
Read the following description of the scientific method.

Basic assumptions in science are that natural events have specific causes, those causes can be identified, and natural events follow general rules and patterns. Biologists are scientists who specifically want to understand everything they can about life through the study of living things (**organisms**): the different types of organisms, how organisms are structured, how they work, and how they interact with each other and their environment. The more biologists understand, the easier it is to both categorize and to make predictions about how life will respond and act in the future. The major activities of living things include responsiveness, the acquisition and use of energy, and self-replication. Biologists are scientists who apply fundamental scientific methodology to gain this knowledge about life.

Scientists use various methods to acquire information, then critically analyze their data to discuss with others, and formulate conclusions based on evidence. This process, which is based on inquiry and evidence, is called **the scientific method**. One way to characterize the method is in a series of steps.

I. The scientific method as used in biology begins with observations of the natural world.
II. Observations raise questions in the minds of biologist, which they want to answer. These key questions might be a problem, and may use the questions "why", "how", and/or "what".
III. The biologist will formulate a potential answer to the question, which can be tested. This is the hypothesis.
IV. The scientist projects what will happen in the future. This prediction would be based on a correct hypothesis.
V. The biologist then tests their hypothesis by conducting experiments. Experimentation is central to the scientific method, and the way scientists gain evidence to support their hypotheses.
VI. The results of the experiment are collected and analyzed. Often a graph will be used as a quick visual summary of data.
VII. The biologist will decide if the data from the experiment support their original hypothesis or not. If not, then the biologist will reject the hypothesis.
VIII. Finally, scientists communicate their results and conclusions with others.

## II. B. Practice making observations

*(Qualitative)*

As you read above, scientific study begins with observation. This activity is designed to help you practice making observations in your role as a scientist. There are three stations for you to visit, labeled A, B, and C. Record you observations below.

### Materials

> on side counter
>> station A: terrarium
>> station B: recording and headphones
>> station C: box with opening with unidentified contents

### Procedure

STEP 1. Observe the contents of the terrarium at station A. Identify or describe three different categories of items.

> 1. What do you see in the terrarium?

White rocks, water, green plants

STEP 2. Listen to the recording found at station B. Describe three different sounds.

> 2. What do you hear?

birds, wildlife, running water

STEP 3. Put your hand in the box at station C. Describe three different textures.

> 3. Describe the texture and/or shape of what you are touching in box C.

half tube, tray, acorn, feather felt thing

STEP 4. Reflect upon your observations of the stations.

> 4. What question(s) do you have about what you have just observed? Which of those questions are key to your understanding of the materials at each station?

What is the felt thing?
* What other sounds are @ station B?

The observations you have made were probably mostly **qualitative** and descriptive in nature. Qualitative data can often be in the form of words, pictures or objects. For example, "the fluffy pillow is soft." As a scientist, you will be asked to conduct experiments using measured amounts of materials, so that you can obtain **quantitative** data which is in the form of numbers and statistics. An example of quantitative data would be "the 35cm X 35cm pillow weighs 1 kg."

## III. USING EQUIPMENT TO MEASURE

### III. A. Laboratory equipment

Commonly used laboratory glassware and instruments are on display on the side counter.

**Materials**
- on side counter
  - beaker
  - forceps
  - graduated cylinders (10-mL and 100-mL)
  - hot plate with Erlenmeyer flask, water, and stir bar
  - dropper bottle
  - meter stick
  - microscope slides: depression, plain
  - Petri dish
  - pipettes with pipette pump: 5-mL and 10-mL
  - scale with weigh boat
  - test tubes in test tube rack, test tube holder
  - watch glass
  - water bath with thermometer

**Procedure**
Go to the side counter to view the glassware and instruments on display. Complete Table 1.1 on the next page by using a checkmark to select the proper usage for each piece of glassware or instrument, or fill in the usage in the last column.

**Table 1.1 Usage of common laboratory equipment**

| | measure mass | measure volume (liquid) | other (specify what) |
|---|---|---|---|
| beaker | | ✓ | not most accurate measure |
| forceps | ✓ | | Pick stuff up |
| graduated cylinders (10-mL and 100-mL) | | ✓ | accurate |
| hot plate with Erlenmeyer flask and stir bar | | ✓ | not as accurate as graduated cylinder |
| dropper bottle | ✓ | | move liquid to |
| meter stick | | | |
| microscope slides: depression, plain and coverslips | | | |
| Petri dish | ✓ | | grow/hold things |
| pipettes with pipette pump: 5-mL and 10-mL | | ✓ | very accurate each marked mils |
| scale with weigh boat | | | |
| test tubes in test tube rack, test tube holder | | ✓ | |
| watch glass | | | |
| water bath with thermometer | | | 80℃ heat stuff |

### III. B. Using the metric system

### Procedure

The international system of measurement is the metric system. In this exercise, you will become more familiar with this system as you estimate sizes and measure common objects.

The measurements relating to length, volume and mass in the metric system are based on factors of 10. There are base units for each type of measurement and they are given the value of $10^0$ or 1. Prefixes are used in front of these base units to alter the values by factors of ten.

On a scale from large to small, the units and their abbreviations and equivalents to the base unit are seen in Table 1.2 below. The prefix symbols can be used with any of the base units (m, L, g) to define length, volume, and mass respectively so that the value, if greater or lesser than the base unit, will include the base unit type plus the abbreviation as a prefix. For example: when measuring in thousandths, "milli" is used. Milli- = $10^{-3}$, and is abbreviated "m". A thousandth of a meter is mm, a thousandth of a liter is mL, and a thousandth of a gram is mg.

### Table 1.2 The metric system

| Prefix | Prefix | $10^n$ | Base Unit Equivalents | Common |
|--------|--------|--------|-----------------------|--------|
| mega | M | $10^6$ | 1000000 | million |
| kilo | k | $10^3$ | 1000 | thousand |
| hecto | h | $10^2$ | 100 | hundred |
| deca | da | $10^1$ | 10 | ten |
| Base unit (m, L, g) | | $10^0$ | 1 | one |
| deci | d | $10^{-1}$ | 0.1 | tenth |
| centi | c | $10^{-2}$ | 0.01 | hundredth |
| milli | m | $10^{-3}$ | 0.001 | thousandth |
| micro | μ | $10^{-6}$ | 0.000001 | millionth |

(Appendix A has a more extensive table of metric units, and Appendix B has examples and practice problems for converting between units.)

Careful measurement ensures **accuracy**, the true measure. Each measuring device has markings or readouts that conform to a standard. The user can approximate an additional last place value with marked instruments like graduated cylinders, pipettes, and rulers. With digital devices, the last digit shown is considered an approximated place value. It is important as a scientist to use instruments correctly and record measurements as accurately as possible. Always record the measurement to the degree of accuracy supported by an instrument.

### Determination of Mass

### Materials

       on side counter
             0.5 L of water
             three containers labeled A, B, C, each containing dried beans
             scale

       on your lab bench
             scale with weigh boat
             penny
             beaker of salt
             metal scoop
             used salt container

### Procedure
The metric unit for measuring mass is the **gram (g)**.

STEP 1. Using the scale and a weigh boat, you will determine the mass of a penny. First place the weigh boat on the scale and press the "tare" or "zero" key. Doing this, the scale recalibrates to zero. Place the penny in the weigh boat, and record the number on the display.

5.  Mass of penny:

      *2.48 grams*

6.  What is the unit of measure on the scale?

      *grams*

7.  How many decimal places are shown?

      *2 (two)*

STEP 2. Place a weigh boat on the scale, press tare, and then pour salt (chemical formula NaCl) from the container into the boat until you have 3.80 g. If you go over, use the scoop to remove excess salt. *Put any excess salt into the used salt container on your lab bench; never return material to a supply jar.*

8. Have one your lab partners check your work and initial that you completed it here.

This amount of salt provides the recommended sodium intake for a healthy adult (3.80 g of salt contains 1.50 g of sodium).

STEP 3. Add salt from the container into the boat until you have 5.20 g.

9. Have one your lab partners check your work and initial that you completed it here.

The second measure, 5.20 g, represents the average daily salt intake of adults. According to the Center for Disease control, "Americans eat too much sodium, commonly consumed as salt. High sodium consumption raises blood pressure. High blood pressure is a major risk factor for heart disease and stroke, the nation's first and third leading causes of death, respectively." (www.cdc.gov/salt)

STEP 4. Go to the side counter and pick up the half liter of water. One-half liter of water weighs 500 grams.

STEP 5. Without touching or lifting, look at containers A, B, and C containing dried beans and record your estimate of its mass below.

10. Container A visual estimate _____150_____ g

    Container B visual estimate _____500_____ g

    Container C visual estimate _____400_____ g

STEP 6. Lift each container.

11. List the containers in sequence of their mass from highest to lowest.

B, C, A,

12. Which container has a mass greater than 500 g?

*B*

STEP 7. Weigh the container using the scale provided on the side counter.

13. Record the true value. Was your estimate correct?

*576g , no*

### Determination of Volume

The metric unit to measure volume is the **liter (L)**. Beakers, graduated cylinders, and pipettes are all used to measure volumes. Graduated cylinders and pipettes will give more accurate readings than beakers. Water has a characteristic that causes it to curve up on glassware; this curve is called a **meniscus**. Liquids are measured at the *base* of the meniscus.

**Figure 1.1 Measuring at the base of the meniscus**

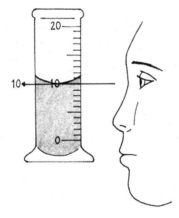

### Materials

on side counter
        25 mL graduated cylinder with water

on your lab bench
        Erlenmeyer flask with red-colored solution
        5 mL pipette with pipetter
        three test tubes in test tube rack
        50 mL beaker
        scale

on instructor's bench
        waste container for red-colored solution

**Procedure**

STEP 1. Find the 25 mL graduated cylinder with water on display at the side counter. Observe and record the amount of water in the graduated cylinder.

14. Record the amount of water in the graduated cylinder here.

*14.5mL*

STEP 2. Return to your lab bench. A pipette is used to measure precise volumes of a solution. To measure and transfer a solution, place the tip of the pipette below the surface of the liquid. Use your thumb to roll the pipette pump to pull up the liquid into the pipette. To transfer the measured liquid into a new receptacle, use your thumb to roll the pump in the opposite direction. Practice pipetting by transferring 3 mL of the red solution provided into each of the three test tubes. During the semester, you will be pipetting liquids often.

15. Have one of your lab partners initial that you completed this pipetting practice here.

STEP 3. Discard the waste red-colored water into the waste container at the instructor's bench.

STEP 4. Determine the weight of 20 mL of water. Use the graduated cylinder, a beaker, and the scale.

16. Explain how you will do STEP 4 with the materials listed.

*Load water into 50mL beaker, transfer into graduated cyclender. 20mL zeroed onto scale*

17. Conduct your experiment and then record the weight of 20 mL of water here.

*19.77g*

18. Mathematically determine the mass of 1 mL of water. Start your calculation using the results of the experiment above weighing 20 mL of water.

*.98 g*

## Determination of Temperature

The common system for temperature measurement is **Celsius** (°C). Water freezes at 0 °C and boils at 100°C. Room temperature is between 20 and 25 °C and normal human body temperature is 37 °C. Throughout the semester you will typically be conducting experiments at 4 °C (ice water), 20 °C, and 37 °C.

### Materials
    on instructor's bench
        ice water bath with thermometer
        body temperature water bath with thermometer
        room temperature test tube rack with thermometer

### Procedure
Observe the three temperature stations set up on the instructor's bench.

19. What equipment is used to establish correct temperatures for experiments?

*Water baths, ice baths, Thermometers*

20. What is the current temperature of the room, in degrees Celsius?

*22 °C*

## Determination of Length

The metric unit to measure length is the **meter (m)**.

### Materials
    on your lab bench
        meter stick
        metric ruler
        food box

### Procedure
STEP 1. At your lab bench, pick up the meter stick. Note the graduations on the stick. There are 100 centimeters (cm) in a meter. There are 1000 millimeters (mm) in a meter.

STEP 2. Compare the food box on your bench to the meter stick.

21. Is the length of the box less than or larger than a meter?

NO

If the box is half the length of the stick, the food box is 50 cm, since there are 100 cm in one meter.

22. Is the box greater or less than 50 cm?

~~2~~ less

STEP 3. Now, measure the length of the food box exactly, using the meter stick or metric ruler. The marking detail on your instrument provides the degree of accuracy you can attain with that instrument. For example, if the ruler has marks for each millimeter, it is accurate to the millimeter, and you may estimate one additional place value.

23. Record your results in both meters and centimeters.

length __.283__ m        Use ladder

length __28.3__ cm

STEP 4. Measure the other two dimensions of the box using the meter stick or a smaller metric ruler.

24. Record your data, remembering to always include the unit of measure.

width __19.7__

depth __6__

## IV. DESIGNING AN EXPERIMENT: THE SCIENTIFIC METHOD IN PRACTICE

Now that you are familiar with the basics of the scientific method, some common equipment available in the laboratory, and measurement techniques, you will make observations, then design and conduct your first scientific experiment. If you look around the room, you will notice that your fellow classmates have a variety of heights. If their heights vary, could there be other physical traits that vary as the height varies?

### IV. A. Observation

**Materials**

> on side counter
>> height chart on side wall

> on your lab bench
>> meter stick
>> tape measure

### Procedure
Using a height chart or meter sticks, measure the height of 12 students in centimeters (cm). Record student names and heights in the first two columns of Table 1.3 on the next page.

### IV. B. Formulating a hypothesis

### Procedure
Formulate a hypothesis about how height could be related to one of the following traits: arm length, head circumference, pulse rate, hand length, or palm width.

> 25. Write the hypothesis here:

### Testing your hypothesis

### Procedure
STEP 1. Design an experiment to test your hypothesis.

> 26. Write out your procedure. Be sure to include all equipment to be used.

metrics on based on 10ths

1. draw a seven step staircase

2. King henry died monday drinking chocolate milk

Quiz question - How many cm is 73.2 kilometers

3. rewrite given # w/ decimal

4. count # of steps of where you are to where you wannago.

5. move decimal pt. # steps to right

(Meter-distance)

K-kilo
H-Hecto
D-Deka
M-meter/liter/gram
D-deci
C-centi
M-mili

Right down

up the 1st

73.2

Right down

73.2

up left

STEP 2. Conduct your experiment and record your data in the last column of Table 1.3.

**Table 1.3 Student height and associated variable data**

| student name | height (cm) | variable (          ) |
|---|---|---|
|  |  |  |
|  |  |  |
|  |  |  |
|  |  |  |
|  |  |  |
|  |  |  |
|  |  |  |
|  |  |  |
|  |  |  |
|  |  |  |
|  |  |  |
|  |  |  |

## IV. C. Results: graphing your experimental data

In this section, you will learn how to represent data. Graphs are used by scientists to provide a quick visual summary of data. Graphs are usually easier to grasp than long lists of numbers found in tables. The graph you will prepare will use the data from your experimental results. Graph paper is located at the end of this lab. See also Appendix H, preparing a simple graph.

### Procedure

STEP 1. Sort your data by rearranging the values from the shortest to tallest student in Table 1.4 on the next page. *Be sure to keep associated data pairs together*, i.e. a student's name will transfer with their associated test variable result.

Student heights were your starting point and what you controlled in your experiment. They become your **independent** variable in this setting. You selected another variable to test. The test results of the selected variable are dependent on your height data. That second variable is therefore the **dependent** variable in this experiment.

STEP 2. Now you can prepare a scattergram of the data. A scattergram is a graph representing the distribution of two variables in a sample population. One variable is plotted on the vertical axis; the second is plotted on the horizontal. You place a mark on the graph where each independent value intersects with its dependent value. Graph paper is located at the end of this lab.

> 27. Which column represents the independent variable, which will go on the horizontal axis (x-axis)?

STEP 3. Title your graph with information to describe both the independent and dependent values, and label each axis with the variable and units used.

## IV. D. Analysis of the experimental results

### Procedure

Analyze your results and decide if your data *support* your original hypothesis from question #25.

> 28. If your data do not support your hypothesis, and you *reject* your hypothesis, propose a new hypothesis and experiment to test it. (Refer also to section II. A.)

**Table 1.4  Student data sorted by increasing height**

| student name | height (cm) | variable (          ) |
|---|---|---|
|  |  |  |
|  |  |  |
|  |  |  |
|  |  |  |
|  |  |  |
|  |  |  |
|  |  |  |
|  |  |  |
|  |  |  |
|  |  |  |
|  |  |  |
|  |  |  |

## IV. E. Communication

### SUMMARY QUESTION

Restate your hypothesis, and describe your experimental design, results, and analysis. One member of your group may be asked to share this with the class during discussion.

**POST-LAB QUESTIONS**                      **Name** _____

1. How does evidence fit into the steps of the scientific method?

2. Give an example of a type of *qualitative* measurement you took in lab.

3. What equipment would you use to accurately measure the volume of liquid in a glass of soda?

4. What common temperatures are used in the lab for experiments?

5. How does the metric system help with *quantitative* measurements?

6. What is the purpose of graphing your results?

# THE CELL

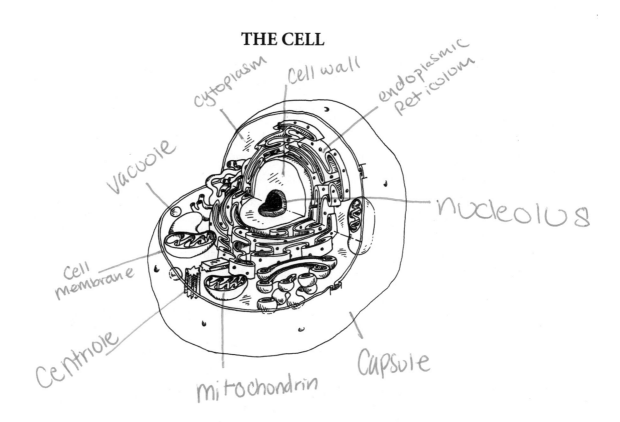

cytoplasm

Cell wall

endoplasmic Reticulum

vacuole

nucleolus

Cell membrane

Centriole

mitochondrin

Capsule

What are organisms made of? What characteristics do organisms of all types have in common? How are they different? How does a biologist examine organisms? These questions will form the framework for your activities in today's lab.

What are organisms made of? All organisms are made of one or more **cells**. The cell is the smallest unit that exhibits the properties of life. All cells come from other cells. These three statements are the components of the **cell theory**, the first theory of biology. You will learn about the general appearance of a cell, its major components and how they work, and compare some different types of cells in today's lab.

What characteristics do organisms of all types have in common? Three key characteristics of life are the ability to maintain homeostasis, to be metabolic, and to have growth. **Homeostasis** is the process by which organisms respond to their environment to maintain their internal conditions. All organisms need to obtain energy to control the chemical processes of their bodies. The term **metabolism** refers to the compilation of the life-sustaining chemical processes. In addition, all organisms **grow** and reproduce. Three major components of a cell perform these three main activities. The **plasma membrane** is in contact with the environment and participates in homeostasis. The plasma membrane manages the internal environment by responding to changing environmental conditions and selectively controlling what goes into or out of the cell. The metabolism of the cell occurs primarily in the **cytoplasm**, the liquid inside the plasma membrane that may include ribosomes, organelles, vesicles, and other inclusions. Control of cellular activities, growth, and reproduction is the responsibility of the DNA of a cell. DNA is located in a central region within an additional membrane, creating a defined **nucleus**, or without a membrane, in what is called the **nucleiod** region.

How does a biologist examine organisms? One way that biologists examine organisms or their components is by looking at cells under a microscope. A compound light microscope uses multiple lenses to magnify objects. In today's lab you will learn how to use the compound light microscope, observe different types of cells from prepared slides, prepare specimens for examination, and examine and compare the activities of microscopic unicellular and multicellular organisms.

**PRE-LAB QUESTIONS**

Name *Sarah Campos*

1. What is a cell?

   *Smallest unit that*

2. How do you know something is alive?

3. How do biologists examine organisms?

**STUDENT LEARNING OUTCOMES**

Upon completion of today's lab, you will be able to do the following:

    I.   properly use a compound light microscope,
   II.  discuss the components of a cell, and compare the general characteristics of cells from the three domains of life,
  III. prepare a wet mount slide of specimens, and
  IV. observe live microorganisms under a microscope.

## I. THE COMPOUND LIGHT MICROSCOPE

The compound light microscope has multiple lenses to magnify an object. The lenses that will be next to your eyes are called the **ocular lenses**. The other lenses are located on a rotating nosepiece and will be close to the object you will be looking at, so they are called the **objective lenses**. The magnification factor for each lens is printed on the lens. Light passes through an object and is magnified by both lenses, so the *total* **magnification** is the product of the magnification factor of each lens.

Objects to be viewed in a compound light microscope are prepared in very thin sections and placed on a glass microscope slide. The slide is placed on the **stage**. Light passes from the lamp through a **condenser** to the object. The amount of light passing through an object can be controlled. The light-intensity knob controls the total amount of light. You will be able to alter the resolution of your image by adjusting the light with the **iris diaphragm** lever found just beneath the stage. **Resolution** is in the ability to distinguish between two points on the object; therefore, the greater the resolution, the more detail you can observe. The iris diaphragm controls the diameter of the light beam passing through the object, and is readjusted each time you change the objective lens.

Appendix C is a labeled photograph of your microscope. A step-by-step procedure for using the compound light microscope is located in Appendix D.

The following activities will help you become more comfortable with the use of the compound light microscope.

**Materials**
    on your lab bench
        compound light microscope (under your lab bench)
        lens paper
        Kimwipes
        prepared slides:
        three-colored threads
        the letter "e"

**Procedure**
STEP 1. Remove a compound light microscope from underneath your lab bench using two hands, one underneath its base, and gently place it on your lab bench. Plug it in, and follow along as your instructor introduces you to its parts and their functions. *Use only lens paper to clean the microscope lenses.*

STEP 2. Select a three colored threads slide from the slide box on your lab bench. Use a Kimwipe to clean off the slide. It is good practice to always clean your prepared slides with a Kimwipe before observation.

STEP 3. Place the microscope slide with three colored threads on the stage of the microscope. Move the stage upward using the coarse focus knob. Adjust the light intensity to a midpoint value using the light intensity knob. Open the iris diaphragm. Starting with the lowest magnification, use the coarse knobs and stage knobs to put the crossed threads in the center of your **field of view,** the area you can see through the microscope. Look through both ocular lenses. You may have to adjust the distance between the ocular lenses to accommodate your eyes.

1. What is the total magnification of your microscope?

   40X (red Objective)

2. Are all three threads in focus throughout the field of view?

   NO

STEP 4. Without lowering the stage, change to the 10X objective lens by rotating the nosepiece until the lens clicks into place. Use the fine focus knob to focus your image, and adjust the iris diaphragm for the sharpest resolution by slowly closing it while looking through the ocular lenses.

3. Do the threads stay in focus along their entire length?

   NO

What is demonstrated by the three-thread slide at different magnifications is a change in the **depth of field**, or resolving power through the depth of the image.

STEP 5. Without lowering the stage, move the 40X objective into place. Use the fine focus knob to focus your image, and adjust the iris diaphragm for the sharpest resolution.

4. What is the total magnification of your microscope now?

   100X (yellow)

5. How does the depth of field change as the total magnification increases?

It decreases

6. How does the field of view change as the total magnification increases?

the field decreases,

STEP 6. Place a microscope slide with the letter "e" on the stage of the microscope. Starting with the lowest magnification, use the stage knobs to put the "e" in the center of your field of view.

7. What is the total magnification of your microscope?

40 X

STEP 7. Without lowering the stage, change to the 10X objective lens. Use the fine focus knob to focus your image, and adjust the iris diaphragm for the sharpest resolution. While looking through the microscope at your specimen, move the stage to the right with the horizontal stage knob.

8. Which direction did the "e" appear to move?

to the left

9. Describe the change in the appearance of the letter "e" as you increased magnification.

you can see the paper fibers

STEP 8. Look at the position of the letter "e", and then slightly move the forward/back stage knob so that the stage moves away from you. Look again at your slide through the microscope.

10. Which direction did the letter "e" move?

towards me and away from me.

## II. THE THREE DOMAINS OF LIFE

How are organisms different? There are three main groups, or **domains**, of life. We sort different organisms into categories based partly on the appearance of their cells. Two of these domains include only single-celled, or **unicellular**, organisms. These domains are Bacteria and Archaea. The DNA in organisms of these two domains is located in nucleoid regions. Members of these domains are called **prokaryotes** because of this feature. The third domain is Eukarya, and members of this domain have a membrane-bound nucleus. Organisms with their DNA contained in a nucleus are referred to as **eukaryotes**. Eukaryotes also contain other membrane-bound regions called **organelles** that separate activities of the cell. Some eukaryotes are unicellular, and some are multicellular.

11.  What is the main difference between a eukaryote and a prokaryote?

### II. A. Domain Bacteria

**Materials**

on side counter
charts of bacteria
model of prokaryotic cell

on your lab bench
prepared slides:
mixed smear of three bacterial shapes (domain Bacteria)
mixed blue-green algae (domain Bacteria, phylum Cyanobacteria)
compount light microscope

**Procedure**

STEP 1. Go to the display on the side counter showing different types of bacteria. Some of the bacteria have fine, hair-like projections called **flagella** that whip back and forth for creating movement. **Pili** help bacteria stick to other organisms.

12.  LABEL the following structures on the bacterial cell in Figure 2.1 on the next page: plasma membrane, nucleiod region, cytoplasm, flagellum, pili, cell wall.

**Figure 2.1 A bacterial cell**

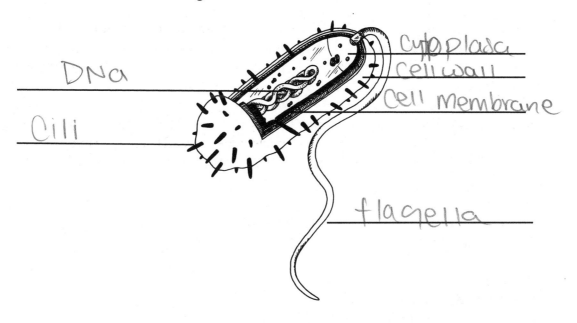

DNa

Cili

Cytoplada

cell wall

cell membrane

flagella

STEP 2. Return to your lab bench. Open the microscope slide box on your lab bench and select the prepared slide of three bacterial shapes, place it on your microscope, and adjust for the best view. Remember to start on the lowest magnification, locate, and focus on your specimen before moving to higher magnifications.

13.   What is the total magnification you need to use to see the shapes clearly?

14.   DRAW several shapes of bacteria here.

Cyanobacteria are among the most important organisms on Earth. Two reasons they are important include their ability to (1) produce oxygen, and (2) transform the element nitrogen from the atmosphere to a useful form for other organisms. Organisms use nitrogen to make important molecules such as proteins and DNA.

STEP 3. Select from the microscope slide box on your lab bench the prepared slide of "mixed blue-green algae" (cyanobacteria) and place it on your microscope.

15. Describe the structures of the cyanobacterium slide (labeled mixed blue-green algae).

## II. B. Domain Archaea

### Materials
on side counter
chart of the three domains of life

on your lab bench
prepared slide:
mixed specimens from domain Archaea
compound light microscope

Members of the domain Archaea live in some of the most extreme environments on the planet, such as hot sulfur springs, extremely salty water, and the digestive tract of some animals to help them digest plant material.

### Procedure
Select from the microscope slide box on your lab bench the prepared slide of archaea for observation on the microscope.

16. Describe the archaean.

17. What similarities and differences do you see between members of the domains Bacteria and Archaea?

## II. C. Domain Eukarya

Biologists sort organisms into groups, called taxa. There is a hierarchy of taxa, with each level containing all those in the lower levels. For example, the domain Eukarya includes many kingdoms, including Animalia, Plantae, Fungi, and Chlorophyta. The highest level is the domain, then comes kingdom, then comes phylum. The species is the smallest category of taxa, so there are large numbers of species in each domain. **Appendix G** lists the hierarchical classification for the wolf. To refer to a member of a species, biologists use a two-part nomenclature, the **binomial**, which identifies the organism by both the genus and the species. Both parts of the binomial are italicized, for example, people are of the species *Homo sapiens*. In the domain Eukarya, some species have only a single cell, like all species in the two prokaryotic domains, while other eukaryotic species have many cells. We use the term **unicellular** if an organism has one cell, and **multicellular** if an organism has more than one cell.

**Materials**

on side counter
   chart depicting taxonomic hierarchy of the polar bear
   model and charts of an animal cell (domain Eukarya, kingdom Animalia)
   model and charts of a plant cell (domain Eukarya, kingdom Plantae)
   herbarium specimens of algae
   chart of Fungi phyla

on your lab bench
   prepared slide:
   desmid (a representative alga)

STEP 1. Go to the side counter to see the taxonomic hierarchy of the polar bear.

18. Complete the taxonomic hierarchy for a polar bear to the species level.

domain Eukarya

19. What is the binomial for the polar bear?

STEP 2. Compare the animal and plant cell diagrams and/or models.

20. What structures do the plant cells have that are different from the animal cells?

21. How do the cells of organisms in the domain Eukarya compare to organisms from the other two domains?

STEP 3. Observe the prepared slide of desmids, an alga. Algae are found in kingdoms in the domain Eukarya.

22. Describe the structure of the algae.

STEP 4. Look at the animal cell model carefully.

23. LABEL the following structures on the animal cell in Figure 2.2 on the next page: plasma membrane, nucleus, cytoplasm, mitochondrion, Golgi apparatus, endoplasmic reticulum, ribosome.

## Figure 2.2 An animal cell

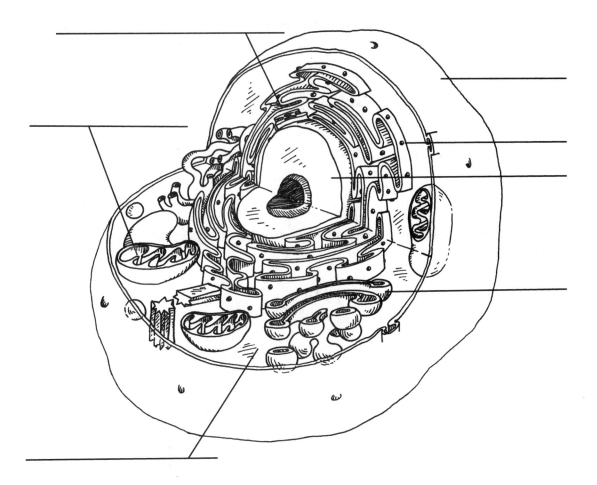

## III. PREPARING SPECIMEN SLIDES

**Materials**

on side counter
> *Elodea* sp.
> dropper bottle with iodine
> dropper bottle with methylene blue
> sterilized toothpicks
> plain microscope slides
> coverslips
> used slide container

on your lab bench
> Kimwipes
> lens paper
> compound light microscope

**Procedure**

STEP 1. Go to the side counter, take a plain microscope slide and a coverslip from where the *Elodea* sp. specimen is located. Prepare a **wet mount** of a small portion of the organism *Elodea* sp. in the following manner: use the dropper to place a drop of iodine on the center of the microscope slide, then pull off a single leaflet from the *Elodea* and place it so it lays flat in the iodine. Place a coverslip at a 45° angle on the slide next to the specimen, and then let it fall over the specimen. Observe your specimen with the compound light microscope at your lab bench.

24. What is the total magnification you need to use to see structures easily?

40X

25. DRAW several cells of the leaflet below. What are the green structures you see?

26. Is *Elodea* sp. a prokaryote or eukaryote? How do you know this?

Prokaryote - it has no nucleus

27. What structures do you observe that help you identify *Elodea* sp. as a plant?

rectangular cell walls

STEP 2. Go to the animal cell preparation area on the side counter. Prepare a wet mount of an animal cell by placing a drop of methylene blue on the center of a plain microscope slide. Rub the inside of your cheek with the tip of a sterilized toothpick and then swirl the tip of the toothpick in the drop of methylene blue on your slide. Place a coverslip at a 45° angle on the slide next to the drop, and then let it fall over the sample.

STEP 3. Observe your specimen with the compound light microscope.

28. What is the total magnification you need to use to see structures easily?

10 X

29. DRAW several cheek cells below, and LABEL the plasma membrane, nucleus, and cytoplasm.

30. What does your cheek cell have in common with the plant cell?

*Cell membrane*

31. How does your cheek cell differ from the plant cell?

*It is a Eukaryote - has a nucleus and no cell walls*

STEP 4. Place all used toothpicks and used slides in the sharps container on the side counter.

## IV. OBSERVING LIVE MICROORGANISMS

In this activity, you will study *Stentor* sp. and rotifers. "Rotifer" is a common name, like "dog" or "cat". Both of these microscopic species are in the domain Eukarya. In this activity, you will compare these two microscopic organisms.

### Materials
on side counter
> specimen jar with *Stentor* sp.
> specimen jar with rotifers
> plain microscope slides
> coverslips
> disposable pipettes
> used slide container
> Congo-red colored yeast in dropper bottle

on your lab bench
> Kimwipes
> lens paper
> compound light microscope

### Procedure
STEP 1. Go to the side counter where the live microorganisms are located. Using a dropper, place one drop of the food provided (Congo red colored yeast) on the center of a clean microscope slide.

STEP 2. Transfer a drop from the specimen container of *Stentor* sp. onto the microscope slide with the yeast. (You may be more likely to find *Stentor* sp. near the food supply in the container.) Cover with a coverslip.

STEP 3. Return to your lab bench and place the slide on your microscope. Adjust the light and magnification so that you can locate your specimen.

32. What is the total magnification you need to use to see structures on the *Stentor* sp. clearly?

100

*Stentor* sp. is grouped with other organisms called ciliates because it has short, fine, hair-like structures called **cilia** around its **gullet** (concave opening for food) that beat to bring food particles into its body.

33. Is *Stentor* a unicellular or multicellular organism?

Unicellular

34. DRAW *Stentor* sp. and describe what you see.

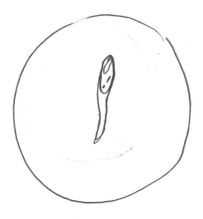

STEP 4. Go to the side counter where the live microorganisms are located. Obtain a clean microscope slide, and then transfer a drop from the specimen container of rotifers onto the slide. Cover with a coverslip.

STEP 5. Return to your lab bench and place the slide on your microscope. Adjust the light and magnification so that you can locate your specimen.

35. What is the total magnification you need to use to see the structures of the rotifer clearly?

400 X

36. What structures do you see that are different then the *Stentor* sp.? Use descriptive terms for the structures if you do not know the technical terms.

Cilia rotators

37. DRAW and LABEL the structures of a rotifer here.

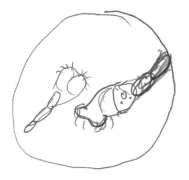

STEP 6. After viewing the rotifers, formulate a hypothesis to explain how they eat.

38. Hypothesis: grab food w/ their pili and shoved in their gullet

STEP 7. Test your hypothesis. Go to the side counter where the live microorganisms are located. Using a dropper, place one drop of the food provided (Congo-red colored yeast) on the center of a clean microscope slide.

STEP 8. Transfer a drop from the specimen container of the rotifers onto the microscope slide with the yeast. Cover with a coverslip.

STEP 9. Return to your lab bench and place the slide on your microscope. Adjust the light and magnification so that you can locate your specimens and watch them eat.

39. Does the evidence support your hypothesis?

*yes*

40. How are rotifers similar to *Stentor* sp.?

*No Both have cilli*

41. How are rotifers different than *Stentor* sp.?

*they are multicellular*

STEP 10. Dispose of your used specimen slides and coverslips into the used slide container on the side counter with the microorganisms.

**SUMMARY QUESTION**

Explain how to prepare a specimen slide of pond water and adjust a microscope for the best image. Identify at least three interesting structures you might see under the microscope in a drop of pond water. One member of your group may be asked to share this with the class during discussion.

**POST-LAB QUESTIONS**                    **Name** _____

1.  What are three general activities that all living cells do?

2.  What is the name of the part of the microscope where your slide is placed?

3.  How can you adjust the light on the microscope to best view your slide?

4.  Which objective lens is used to first scan your object?

5.  How do you determine the total magnification with which you are looking at your specimen?

6.  What is the relationship between magnification and the size of the field of view? What is the relationship between magnification and depth of field?

7.  Which organisms among those you saw today were the smallest?

8.  Why do plant cells have different components than animal cells?

*Questions continue on the next page.*

9. Match these cellular structures to their function.

A. plasma membrane
B. chloroplast
C. cytoplasm
D. endoplastmic reticulum
E. Golgi apparatus
F. lysosome
G. mitochondrion
H. nucleolus
I. nucleus
J. ribosome
K. vacuole

_____ the central area containing DNA and surrounded by a membrane

_____ a membranous sac within the cell enclosing water, food, or waste

_____ converts food to usable energy (ATP)

_____ functions in intracellular digestion

_____ contains the cell, and controls entry into, and exit from, the cell

_____ organelle that converts sunlight, $CO_2$ and water into food (site of photosynthesis)

_____ the site of protein synthesis

_____ site of ribosome subunit production

_____ a membranous network involved in the synthesis and processing of cellular materials

_____ a curved stacked membranous network that processes and packages cellular materials

_____ a semifluid substance outside the nucleus where cellular activities occur

# MOVEMENT ACROSS THE PLASMA MEMBRANE

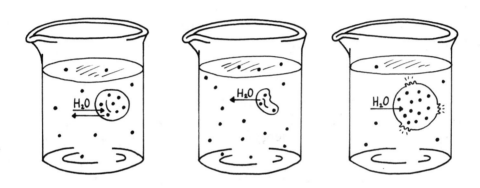

How does the cell acquire the materials it needs? How does the cell minimize the energy required to move substances across the plasma membrane? What determines the rate substances move across the membrane? How does the cell bring in materials that are too large to pass through the membrane? These questions will form the framework for your activities in today's lab.

All cells need substances from the surrounding environment in order to support normal cell functions. These substances will be used to form the complex organic molecules that make up the structures of the cell, and also guide its operation. The plasma membrane separates the cytoplasm from the external environment and also controls the passage of materials into and out of the cell. The plasma membrane is designed so that entry and exit of substances to and from the cell are limited by their size, charge, and the ability of that substance to mix with water, its **hydrophilicity**. The plasma membrane is **selectively permeable**. Small, uncharged and/or lipid materials can move across the membrane by **passive** processes, requiring no energy expenditure from the cell. **Active** processes require cellular energy. Both passive and active processes are used to move materials into and out of the cell.

**Diffusion** is the passive movement of molecules along a concentration gradient, that is, from an area of high concentration to an area of lower concentration. This type of movement requires no input of cellular energy because the higher the concentration of molecules, the greater the frequency of collisions occur, causing the molecules to move away from each other, and toward areas of lesser concentration. Eventually, in a closed system, this random movement will reach **equilibrium** where there is no longer any net movement of the molecules. The rate at which molecules collide and move depends on the size and concentration of the molecules as well as the temperature. Diffusion may be aided by membrane channels which facilitate the movement across the membrane. This may be necessary when the molecules that are diffusing are too large, or too hydrophilic to move on their own accord through the membrane. This type of diffusion is called **facilitated diffusion** and also does not require the input of any cellular energy. The third type of passive movement is called osmosis. **Osmosis** is the movement of water from an area of high water concentration to an area of lower water concentration. Water molecules are very small and will collide with other water molecules creating movement that may be across a membrane. In all types of passive movement, the larger the concentration gradient, the greater the rate of movement will be.

**Active transport** also involves the movement of molecules across a plasma membrane, but in this case the input of cellular energy is required. Active transport involves the use of energy to move molecules across the plasma membrane against a concentration gradient, that is, moving molecules from an area of lower concentration to an area of higher concentration. This is typically done using special membrane transport proteins that use cellular energy to shuttle the molecules. Active transport may also involve creating a vesicle by surrounding the molecules with a membrane, and transporting the vesicle into (**endocytosis**) or out of (**exocytosis**) the cell. The movement of these vesicles requires cellular energy.

**PRE-LAB QUESTIONS**                    Name _Sarah Campos_

1. Why is it necessary for substances to move into or out of the cell?

   to have normal function (cell)

2. What is the function of the plasma membrane?

   Controls passage of materials in/out of cell

3. What is a major difference between diffusion and active transport?

   diffusion - passive movement of molecules, no input of energy

   Active - required cellular energy, movement molecules across plasma

4. Osmosis is the special case of the diffusion of what molecule?

   movement of water from high water concentration to lower water concentration

5. Other than water, what other substances may be transported across the plasma membrane of a cell?

   The vesicle can be transported into endocytosis

## STUDENT LEARNING OUTCOMES

Upon completion of today's lab you will be able to do the following:

    I.   explain how material moves into and out of a cell,
    II.  explain factors that influence the rate of diffusion,
    III. explain osmosis and be able to determine if a cell is in a hypotonic, hypertonic, or isotonic solution,
    IV. describe endocytosis, and
    V.  appropriately graph and interpret the results of collected data.

## I. HOW MATERIAL MOVES INTO AND OUT OF THE CELL WITHOUT USING CELLULAR ENERGY

The passive process of diffusion requires no energy expenditure on the part of the cell. Remember, molecules are in constant random motion in any chemical system that is above absolute zero in temperature. An easily observed manifestation of the forces that cause diffusion is **Brownian movement**. Brownian movement is the oscillatory movement of particles resulting from the chance bombardment of those particles by other molecules in the system.

### Materials
    on your lab bench
        dropper bottle of carmine dye
        plain microscope slides
        coverslips
        compound light microscope

    on instructor's bench
        used slide container

### Procedure
STEP 1. Obtain a dropper bottle of carmine dye and gently shake it, then use the dropper to place a single drop of the dye suspension on a clean glass microscope slide and cover with a coverslip.

STEP 2. Observe the preparation immediately under the microscope. Increase the magnitude up to the high power objective lens (40X).

    1.  Describe the movement that you observe.

little darks moving

2. What is the relationship between particle size and the degree of Brownian movement observed?

*Smaller particles are going to move faster.*

STEP 3. Discard the used microscope slide and coverslip in the used slide container located on the instructor's bench.

## II. FACTORS THAT INFLUENCE THE RATE OF DIFFUSION

In today's lab, you will explore how the rate of diffusion may be affected by a number of factors including the initial concentration of the substance, the degree of the concentration gradient (difference in concentration of that substance from one location to another), and molecular size (as determined by molar mass).

## II. A. The effect of concentration on diffusion rate

In this activity, you will compare the diffusion rate of two different liquid concentrations of the same dye through a semisolid gel. Rates are established by determining the distance traveled in a given time period.

### Materials

on your lab bench

Petri dish with agar gel and two 10-mm wells

wax pencil

dropper bottle with 1% dye (potassium permanganate) solution

dropper bottle with 5% dye (potassium permanganate) solution

### Procedure

STEP 1. Obtain a Petri dish. Notice that one side is filled with agar gel, and there are two wells punched into the gel.

STEP 2. Use the wax pencil to mark the back of the gel-filled plate side of the Petri dish with the numbers 1 and 5. Put these numbers on the edge of the outside of the plate as shown in Figure 3.1. (By placing the numbers on the edge, they will not get covered up when the dye runs through the gel.)

*factor affecting fusion - how fast something diffused*

**Figure 3.1 Petri dish with gel and prepunched wells**

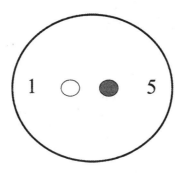

1   ○   ●   5

STEP 3. You are now ready to *fill* the wells with dye. Open the Petri dish. On Table 3.1 below, note the starting time in the box for time 0. Fill well number 1 with the 1% potassium permanganate dye solution, and fill well number 5 with the 5% potassium permanganate dye solution. Use the dropper bottles containing each dye to fill the separate wells in the agar. *Be careful to not overfill the wells but do fill the wells as close to the tops as possible.*

STEP 4. Place the plate with the gel and dye solutions on top of a metric ruler to measure the diameter of the circle of dye as it increases over time. Record the values of the diameter of each circle every 15 minutes for a total of 75 minutes on Table 3.1. You may remove the top of the Petri dish during readings if it fogs up, but otherwise keep it on so the agar and solutions do not dry up.

**Table 3.1 Diameters in mm of two concentrations of dye solutions**

should go faster

| time (minutes) | 1% potassium permanganate | 5% potassium permanganate |
|---|---|---|
| 0 start: | 1 cm | 1 cm |
| 15 | 1.8 cm | 2.2 cm |
| 30 | 2.3 cm | 2.6 cm |
| 45 | 2.5 cm | 2.8 cm |
| 60 | | |
| 75 | | |

STEP 5. Discard the Petri dish in the trash when you have completed the experiment.

STEP 6. Graph the values of the diameters of the two concentrations of dye from 0 to 75 minutes. This will require two sets of data; one for each concentration. Label each axis and add a title. Graph paper is located at the end of this lab.

3. Which is the dependent variable? What are the units of the dependent variable? Which axis on the graph is used for the dependent variable?

4. Compare the rates of diffusion of the two concentrations. What are your results? Explain your answer.

*rate of the 5% went faster because its higher concentration*

5. How many centimeters was the diameter of the 1% dye solution at 45 minutes?

*2.5 cm*

6. Do diffusion rates change over time? Explain your answer.

*yes,*

7. Do you think a solution with a higher contentration or a solution with a lower concentration will move into a cell faster? Explain your answer.

*It was higher concentration*

## II. B. The Effect of mass on diffusion rate

In this activity, you will compare the diffusion rate of two different dyes through a semisolid gel. The two dyes, potassium permanganate and Rose Bengal, have different molar masses. That means, for example, that 500 molecules of potassium permanganate weigh a different amount than 500 molecules of Rose Bengal. Rates are established by determining the distance traveled in a given time period.

**Materials**

on your lab bench

Petri dish with agar gel and two 10 mm wells

wax pencil

dropper bottle with 1% dye (potassium permanganate) solution, molar mass 158 g/mol

dropper bottle with 1% dye (Rose Bengal) solution, molar mass 1018 g/mol

**Procedure**

STEP 1. Obtain a Petri dish containing agar with prepared wells for each of the two dye solutions.

STEP 2. LABEL the bottom of the Petri dish so you know which dye is in which well.

STEP 3. Use the dropper bottles containing each dye to fill the separate wells in the agar. Be careful to not overfill the wells but do fill the wells as close to the tops as possible.

STEP 4. Place the plate with the gel and dye solutions on top of a metric ruler to measure the diameter of the circle of dye as it increases over time. Note the starting time in the box for time 0. Record the values of the diameter of each circle every 15 minutes for a total of 75 minutes on Table 3.2. You may remove the top of the Petri dish during readings if it fogs up, but otherwise keep it on so the agar and solutions do not dry up.

**Table 3.2 Diameters in mm of two dye solutions of different molar mass**

| time (minutes) | 1% potassium permanganate | 1% Rose Bengal |
|---|---|---|
| 0 start: | 1cm | 1cm |
| 15 | 2cm | 1.5cm |
| 30 | 2.3cm | 1.8cm |
| 45 | 2.5cm | 1.9cm |
| 60 | | |
| 75 | | |

1. Brownian movement: random movement of molecules

STEP 5. Discard the Petri dish in the trash when you have completed the experiment.

STEP 6. Graph the values of the diameters of the two dyes from 0 to 75 minutes. Label each axis and add a title. Graph paper is located at the end of this lab.

  8. What is the independent variable in this experiment? Which axis displays the independent variable?

  9. Which of the two dyes used in the experiment diffused more rapidly? Compare their molar masses, provided in the materials section, and explain why.

The rose bengal lower molecule mass because it

## III. OSMOSIS IN DIFFERENT ENVIRONMENTS

Solutions are mixtures containing solvents and solutes. The **solvent** is the substance of greater abundance in the mixture. The **solute** is the substance of lower amount in the mixture. Water functions as a solvent in the cytoplasm. In many cases water is also a solvent in the cell's external environment. Since water molecules are quite small, they will diffuse freely across the plasma membrane. Examples of cellular solutes include salts, starch, and proteins. Most cellular and environmental solutes are too large to freely pass through the plasma membrane by diffusion. The relative concentration of such nondiffusible solutes within the cell as compared to outside of the cell will have an effect upon the direction of water movement. The extracellular environments are designated as hypotonic, isotonic, or hypertonic, depending on the concentration of solutes relative to the inside of the cell.

In a **hypotonic** environment the solute concentration is lower outside the cell than within the cell. In a **hypertonic** environment the solute concentration is much more outside the cell than inside the cell. In an **isotonic** environment the solute concentration is the same inside and outside of the cell.

In this activity, you will observe the process of osmosis as water moves in or out of artificial cells made out of dialysis tubing placed in isotonic, hypotonic, and hypertonic environments. Just as a window screen permits airflow but keeps bugs from moving into your house, dialysis tubing is a screen with very tiny openings. The dialysis tubing is a selectively permeable membrane; it restricts movement across the tubing by size. Water can freely move across the tubing, but sucrose (table sugar) is too big to cross the tubing screen.

**Materials**
> on your lab bench
>> three dialysis tubes with clips
>> three 600-mL beakers
>> 0% (clear), 10% (red), and 20% (blue) sucrose solutions
>> three pipettes, color-coded
>> wax pencil
>> weigh boats
>> scale

**Procedure**

STEP 1. Remove a presoaked dialysis membrane tube. Fold one end down about 10 mm and then fold it again lengthwise and secure with the clip provided. Repeat this process with the other two dialysis tubes. The dialysis tubing will serve to represent a semi-permeable membrane analogous to those found in all cells.

STEP 2. Rub the wet tubing with your thumb and fingers to open your newly made dialysis cell. The sucrose solutions are color-coded for your convenience. Using the appropriate pipette, measure and fill a cell with 15 mL of 0% sucrose solution. After you fill the cell, fold over the open end of the tubing about ten millimeters and secure as before with the clip provided to seal the cell.

STEP 3. In a similar manner to STEP 2, transfer 15 mL of the red 10% sucrose solution into a second dialysis cell, and 15 mL of the blue 20% sucrose solution into a third dialysis cell.

STEP 4. Place a weigh boat on the scale and tare to zero. Record the mass of each of the cells on the scale as the initial mass in spaces provided in Table 3.4 below.

STEP 5. Mark the three 600-mL beakers "1", "2", and "3", using a wax pencil.

STEP 6. Place the blue 20% sucrose cell into beaker #1, the red 10% sucrose cell into beaker #2, and the clear 0% sucrose cell into beaker #3.

STEP 7. Note your start time, then pour enough of the clear 0% sucrose solution to cover the cell in beaker #1. In a similar manner, cover the red 10% sucrose cell in beaker #2 with red 10% sucrose solution. Cover the clear 0% sucrose cell in beaker #3 with blue 20% sucrose solution. Table 3.3 on the next page summarizes your setup.

**Table 3.3 Contents of Dialysis Cells and Beakers**

| beaker number | cell contents | beaker contents |
|---|---|---|
| 1 | 15 mL 20% sucrose | 0% sucrose |
| 2 | 15 mL 10% sucrose | 10% sucrose |
| 3 | 15 mL 0% sucrose | 20% sucrose |

STEP 8. Note the start time in the box for time 0. At 15-minute intervals, for a total time of 75 minutes, remove each of the cells from its beaker, *wipe off excess liquid* and re-weigh the cell with a weigh boat on a tared scale. To determine the net mass change that has occurred at each time point, *subtract the original mass from the value obtained at that time point.* Record both the raw data (measured mass) and calculated net change (mass *change* from *original* value) for all three cells at all of the 15-minute intervals.

STEP 9. Graph the results for each cell as *net mass change over time (shaded cells).* Use different symbols for each set of data points and include a legend and title with your graph. Graph paper is located at the end of this lab.

**Table 3.4. Dialysis cell mass over time (grams)**

| time (minutes) | cell #1 | | cell #2 | | cell #3 | |
|---|---|---|---|---|---|---|
| | mass | change | mass | change | mass | change |
| 0 start: | 28.58g | 0 | 29.07g | 0 | 29.29g | 0 |
| 15 | 29.03 g | +.46 | 30.88g | +1.81 | 31.58g | +2.29 |
| 30 | 28.54g | +.49 | 30.57g | -.29 | 32.97g | +.39 |
| 45 | 27.88g | -.66 | 30.41g | -.18 | 32.98g | +1.01 |
| 60 | 27.13g | -0.75 | 30.48g | +0.07 | 33.68g | +0.70 |
| 75 | | | | | | |

STEP 10. Please clean and return all clips to your lab bench. You may discard the cells you prepared in the trash. You will recover the beaker liquids so they can be reused. Pour the liquids from the beakers into the corresponding bottles. Rinse the beakers and weigh boats and return them to your lab bench.

10. Is the environment established in beaker #1 containing the blue 20% sucrose cell hypotonic, isotonic or hypertonic? How were you able to determine this fact from your data? What is a possible outcome if this was a real, living cell in this type of environment?

*hypotonic, mass Should increase. Cell should burst.*

11. What was the net change in mass over the 75-minute experimental period for cell #2?

*Should not change*

12. Was this change significant compared with the others noted? Explain why or why not.

*No, not enough time.*

13. Is the environment established in the beaker containing cell #3 hypotonic, isotonic or hypertonic? How were you able to determine this fact from your data?

*hypertonic*

14. You filled each cell with 15 mL of solution. How many µL is that?

## IV. ACTIVE TRANSPORT PROCESSES: ENDOCYTOSIS

**Endocytosis** is an example of an active transport process that you will observe in this activity. The unicellular *Amoeba proteus* preys on smaller organisms, like ciliates, found in pond water. The unicellular ciliates are too large to pass directly through the plasma membrane. *Amoeba proteus* moves towards its prey and extends its membrane to surround its prey. The movement of the amoeba's cytoplasm is called cytoplasmic streaming and involves the use of its cytoskeleton and cellular energy. Surrounding the prey with its membrane to engulf it is an example of **phagocytosis** ("cell eating"), a type of active transport called endocytosis.

**Materials**

> on your lab bench
>> prepared slide of *Amoeba proteus*
>> compound light microscope

> on instructor's bench
>> jar with *Amoeba proteus* culture
>> jar with ciliates culture
>> disposable transfer pipettes
>> plain microscope slides
>> coverslips
>> used slide container

**Procedure**

STEP 1. Select the prepared slide of *Amoeba proteus* from your slide box and place it on your compound light microscope. Adjust the light and magnify your specimen until you can see it clearly.

15.  What is a good magnification to use to observe your specimen?

10 X

16.  Describe the specimen.

blob like.

STEP 2. Go to the instructor's bench to obtain live specimens. Be careful not to raise or swirl the culture jars. The best location to find organisms is near their food source. Using the transfer pipette labeled for the ciliates, introduce a small amount of liquid from the ciliate culture onto a plain microscope slide. Use the special transfer pipette for amoebas to add two drops from the *Amoeba proteus* culture to the slide. Cover your slide with a coverslip.

STEP 3. Using the lowest magnification on your compound light microscope, scan the field of view to find an amoeba. Once found, center and magnify your live specimen.

17.  Describe the movement of your specimen.

*Cytoplasmic Streaming*

18.  Describe the actions of the amoeba when it consumes its prey.

*it engulfs it.*

STEP 4. Return the prepared slide to the slide box. Discard your live amoeba slide preparation into the used slide container on the instructor's bench.

**SUMMARY QUESTION**

Summarize the processes of diffusion, osmosis, and endocytosis. Discuss how the factors you studied in this lab can alter the rate of diffusion of a specific substance, and why these processes are important to living cells. One member of your group may be asked to share this with the class during discussion.

#1

15mL 20% (blue)
Solution in bag

200mL clear (0%
Solution in beaker)
   - hypotonic - into cell
   - mass should increase

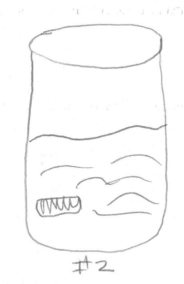

#2

15ml (10%
Solution (red in bag

200mL
of red in beaker
   - ISOTONIC
   - mass should stay same

#3

15mls 0%

Clear in bag
200mls blue in
beaker

-hypertonic - out of cell
   - mass should decrease

**POST-LAB QUESTIONS**                          Name _Sarah Campos_

1. Temperature increases molecular motion. Predict how an increase in temperature from 25° C to 40° C would affect the rate of diffusion of a solute. Explain your answer.

   *Molecules moves faster*
   *diffusion rate increases*

2. Predict the change in the rate of phagocytosis in an amoeba as it goes from warmer water to colder water.

   *Slows down*

3. Why is maintaining a constant temperature through homeostasis important in a human?

   *So we can function properly*

4. Extremely hypotonic or hypertonic environments can prove to be fatal to many cell types. Explain why.

   *hypertonic – it will shrink*
   *hypotonic – it can burst*

5. What would you expect to observe if a suspension of human red blood cells, naturally at 0.9% salt solution, were transferred to a 10% salt solution environment?

   *It should shrivel up.*

6. What structure found in the plant cell is responsible for maintenance of an intact membrane when the cell is placed into a hypotonic environment (e.g., distilled water)?

   *Cell ~~membrane~~ wall is responsible to maintain intact*

*Questions continue on the next page.*

7. By what mechanism might high molar mass chemicals not capable of diffusing gain entrance to the cell across the membrane?

*active transport*

8. A cell is growing in an environment containing 2% sucrose but the cell itself, when analyzed for sucrose content, contains 10% sucrose. What process would provide an explanation for this data?

9. Why is it important for solutions in IV (intravenous) bags to be isotonic relative to the blood?

*So you do not die*

10. LABEL each of the following beakers as examples of cells in hypotonic, isotonic, and hypertonic environments.

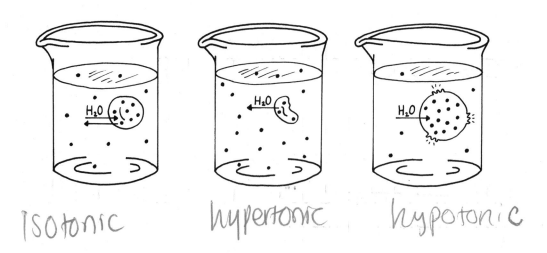

*Isotonic*          *hypertonic*          *hypotonic*

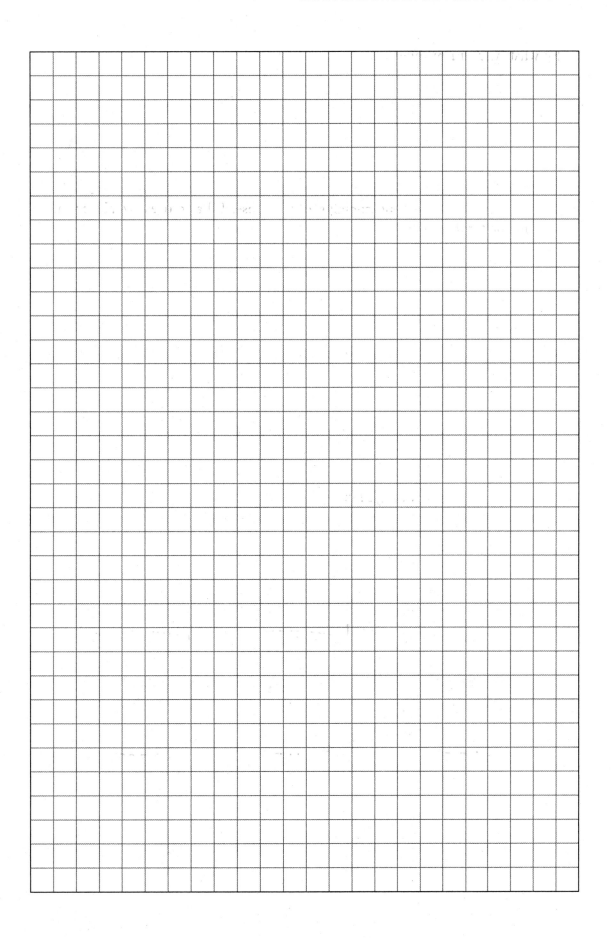

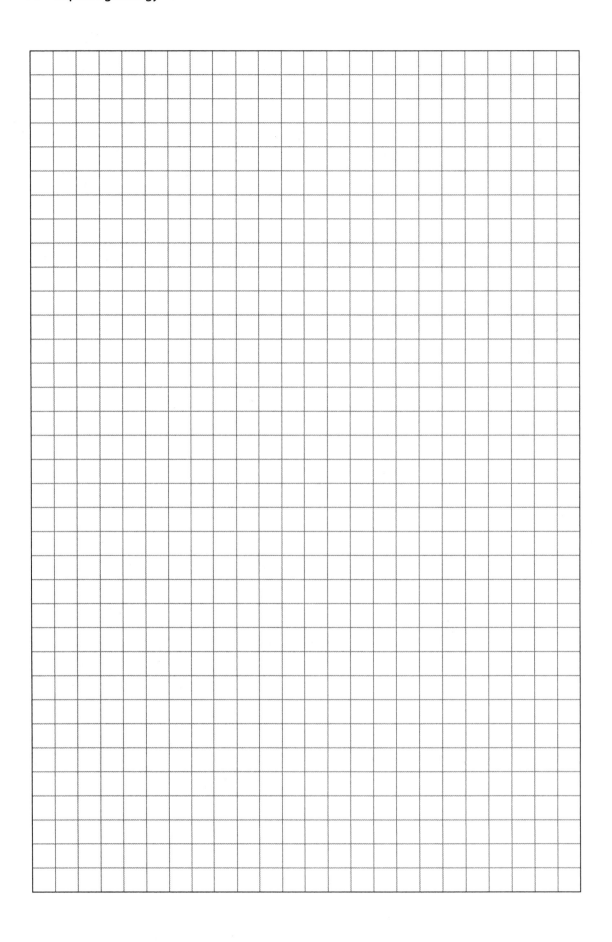

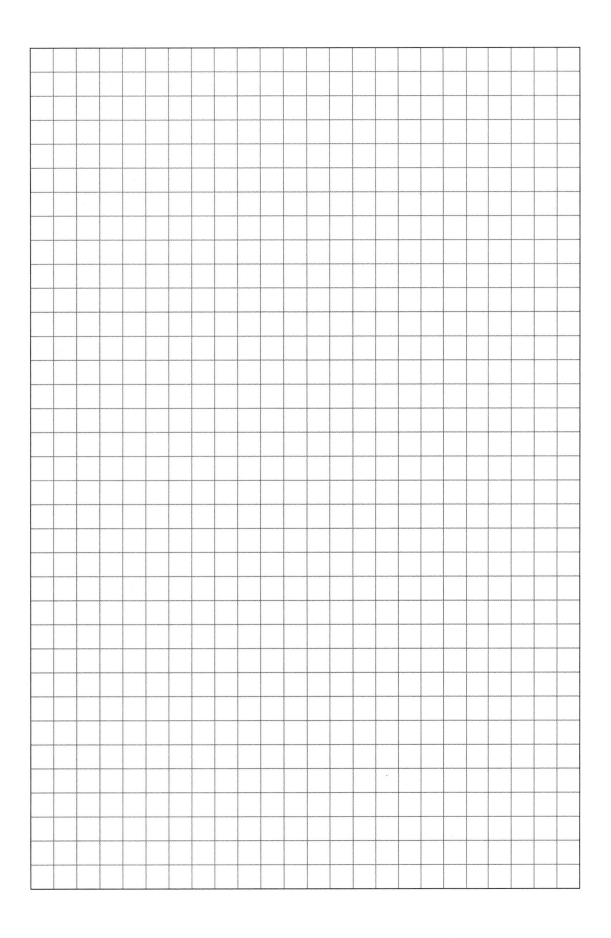

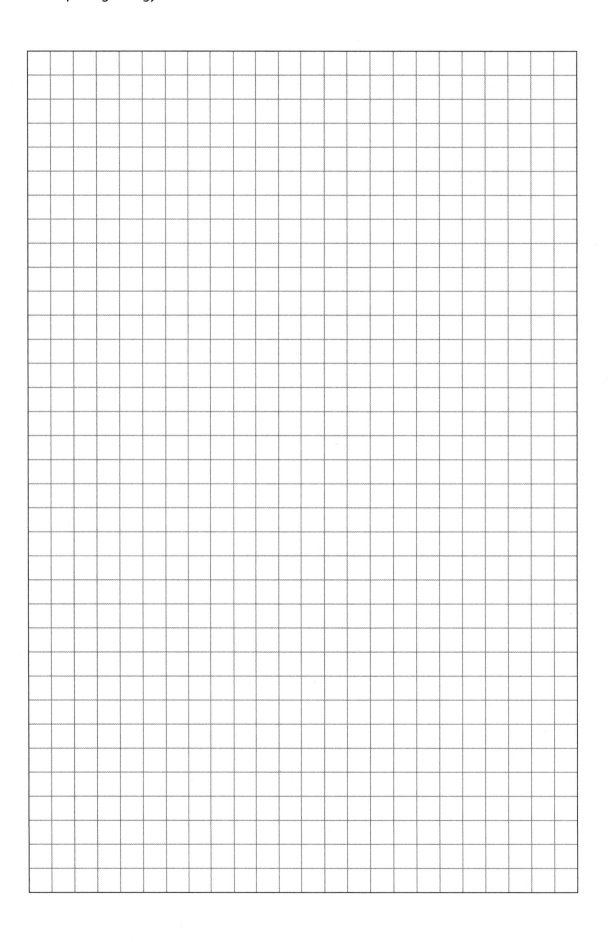

# FACILITATING CHEMICAL REACTIONS WITH ENZYMES

How does a cell make new products in the cytoplasm? What is an enzyme? What is an enzymatic reaction? How can biologists examine the work of an enzyme? These questions will form the framework for your activities in today's lab.

How does a cell make new products in the cytoplasm? Inside the watery cytoplasm, molecules that are brought into the cell may be broken down and then combined with other molecules manufactured by the cell. The molecules are transformed into new products by **chemical reactions**. Chemical reactions are not unique to a cell, but can occur naturally between certain substances if they are put together in the same place, e.g., a beaker. In a chemical reaction, molecules, called **reactants**, interact and form **products**. We can denote this with an equation. If "A" and "B" represent the starting substances, and "C" and "D" represent the final products, then the equation for a chemical reaction is:

$$A + B \quad \rightarrow \quad C + D$$
$$\text{reactants} \qquad \text{products}$$

The arrow indicates the direction of the reaction. Temperature and the concentration of the reactants affect the speed of product formation. Higher temperature increases molecular motion and subsequent collisions between molecules. Similarly, increasing the concentration of the reactants will increase the frequency of collisions.

What is an enzyme? **Enzymes** are called biological catalysts because they make chemical reactions occur faster than if the reaction was to occur without an enzyme. Organisms generally cannot tolerate wide changes in temperature or have excess materials available to speed chemical reactions to the rate required to get their products made in a timely fashion. To perform chemical reactions at a useful rate, without a change in temperature, they use enzymes. What makes enzymes additionally valuable is that enzymes are not changed in the reaction itself, so they can facilitate another reaction.

What is an enzymatic reaction? Each enzyme works only with particular reactants, called **substrates**. In an enzymatic reaction, the substrates are converted to products. The equation for an enzymatic reaction, in contrast to the equation for a chemical reaction, replaces the term "reactants" with "substrates", and includes the name of the enzyme *above* the arrow (since it does not get used up in the reaction).

$$\overset{\text{enzyme}}{A + B \quad \rightarrow \quad C + D}$$
$$\text{substrates} \qquad \text{products}$$

How can biologists examine the work of an enzyme? One way is to use an instrument called a **spectrophotometer** that measures light absorbance. If an enzymatic reaction results in a product with a color change, the amount of product formed can be determined quantitatively with the spectrophotometer.

**PRE-LAB QUESTIONS**                              **Name** _____

1.  What do biologists call reactants in an enzymatic reaction?

2.  Why do organisms need enzymes?

3.  What is the purpose of a spectrophotometer?

4.  Do enzymes become part of the product in an enzymatic reaction? Explain how this benefits the cell.

*Eye protection must be worn throughout today's lab.*

**STUDENT LEARNING OUTCOMES**

Upon successful completion of today's lab you will be able to do the following:

    I.   identify and describe the role of each of the components in an enzymatic reaction,

    II.  use a spectrophotometer

    III. explain factors that affect enzymatic product formation, and

    IV. appropriately graph collected data.

In today's lab, you will run a series of experiments to determine the effect of enzyme and substrate concentration on the rate of the enzymatic reaction by following a reaction that results in a color change. *Eye protection must be worn throughout today's lab.*

## I. THE COMPONENTS OF AN ENZYMATIC REACTION

From the introduction, you know that the components of an enzymatic reaction include enzymes, substrates, and products. Enzymes also exhibit **specificity**, the ability to recognize and bond to only one particular substrate. Conveniently, enzymes are named by their substrates. For example, the enzyme lactase breaks down the sugar lactose.

How do enzymes work? Enzymes are (almost always) proteins consisting of long chains of amino acids that fold to form a 3-dimensional globular shape with an **active site.** Like puzzle pieces, the unique shape of each enzyme at the active site allows only its specific substrate to make a temporary weak bond to the enzyme (see Figure 4.1). Enzymes will then break or make bonds to convert substrates into products without becoming part of the product. Enzymes are not destroyed or changed during this process, so once a reaction is completed, the enzyme is free to facilitate additional reactions of the same type. A little bit of enzyme goes a long way!

**Figure 4.1 Enzyme function**

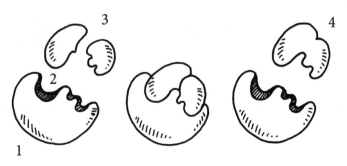

1 = enzyme    2 = active site   3 = substrates   4 = product

In today's lab, you will mix the colorless enzyme, **alkaline phosphatase** with its colorless substrate para-nitrophenyl phosphate. The enzyme will remove phosphate from the substrate to form a yellow-colored product, nitrophenol. A **buffer solution** is used to stabilize the pH of the solution during the reactions. You will stop the reaction by adding a strong base, sodium hydroxide (NaOH), that will disrupt the enzyme shape.

The equation for the general reaction is:

alkaline phosphatase

para-nitrophenyl phosphate    →    nitrophenol + phosphate
(colorless)                              (yellow)

**Materials**

on side counter
eye protection

on your lab bench
bottle with buffer solution at pH 10
bottle with substrate (para-nitrophenyl phosphate)
pipettes labeled for each component above
dispenser pump bottle with sodium hydroxide (NaOH)
dropper bottle with enzyme (alkaline phosphatase)
test tube rack
6 cuvettes (special test tube with superior optical quality)
wax pencil

**Procedure**

STEP 1. *Obtain and use eye protection for this entire lab.*

STEP 2. Obtain a cuvette from the test tube rack. Use the wax pencil to mark the upper portion of the tube with the letter "R" for reaction. This cuvette will be your reaction cuvette.

STEP 3. Using the appropriately labeled pipette, transfer 1.0 mL of the pH 10 buffer solution into the cuvette.

STEP 4. Using the appropriately labeled pipette, add 1.0 mL of substrate to the reaction cuvette with the buffer solution.

STEP 5. Observe the color and clarity of the solution and note it on Table 4.1 on the next page.

STEP 6. Note the time, and then add five (5) drops of enzyme from the dropper bottle into your reaction cuvette. Mix the solution by gently flicking the cuvette.

STEP 7. Every two minutes, for up to 10 minutes or until otherwise instructed, observe the color and intensity of the solution in your reaction cuvette, and note it on the table below.

STEP 8. At 10 minutes or until otherwise instructed, dispense NaOH into the cuvette. The dispenser is preset to deliver 3 mL. *With a flat hand, gently press down on the dispenser and let up only once.* Mix the solution by gently flicking the cuvette.

STEP 9. Place the reaction cuvette with solution into the test tube rack and keep it to use in the next activity.

**Table 4.1 Color change of reaction every two minutes for 10 minutes**

| minutes | color and intensity |
|---|---|
| 0 minutes (before adding enzyme) | Clear    7:02 |
| 2 minutes | Clear |
| 4 minutes | Slight yellow |
| 6 minutes | a Slight more yellow |
| 8 minutes | green/yellow |
| 10 minutes | greenish yellow |

1. What is the name of the enzyme in this reaction? How does that relate to the name of the substrate?

   The enzyme is Alkaline phosphate, it relates to the substrate it worked on

2. Discuss how the color changed over time and what the color change indicated.

   The color change over time became darker in yellow – (the product was formed)

## II. USING THE SPECTROPHOTOMETER

Observing the color change is a qualitative way of following the enzymatic reaction. A quantitative and more objective way of monitoring an enzymatic reaction is to use a **spectrophotometer**. This is a special laboratory apparatus that measures absorption or transmission of a specific wavelength of light. As the enzyme interaction with its substrate increases, the concentration of product in the cuvette increases. The increasing concentration of product reduces the amount of light that is transmitted through the test tube. Light that is not transmitted is absorbed.

In this lab, you will use the spectrophotometer to determine the amount of **light absorbed** by the products. The more product that is produced, the more light is absorbed by the products. In Activity III, you will run several experiments using the same substrate and enzyme to determine how various factors affect the rate of the enzymatic reaction as measured by the production of product.

### II. A. Preparation of a blank

Prior to running experiments you will make a special solution called a **blank**. The blank is a cuvette that contains all the same substances in your reaction, except enzyme and, therefore, it will have no product. The blank is used in the spectrophotometer to calculate and subtract all the absorbance due to the other components in the solution, enabling you to measure the amount of light absorption due to product formation only. You will use the blank in "blanking or zeroing out" the spectrophotometer, just as you could zero out a weigh boat on a scale.

**Materials**
> on side counter
>> eye protection
>
> on your lab bench
>> bottle with buffer solution at pH 10
>> Kimwipes
>> bottle with substrate (para-nitrophenyl phosphate)
>> pipettes labeled for each component above
>> dispenser pump bottle with sodium hydroxide (NaOH)
>> dropper bottle with water
>> cuvette labeled "R" with solution from Activity I
>> cuvettes in test tube rack
>> wax pencil
>
> on instructor's bench
>> hazardous waste container
>> bottle of distilled water

**Procedure**

STEP 1. Select a cuvette from the test tube rack. Mark your cuvette "B" for "blank" with the wax pencil at the upper portion of the cuvette. This cuvette will be your blank cuvette used for the remainder of the lab.

STEP 2. Using the appropriately labeled pipette, transfer 1.0 mL of the pH 10 buffer solution into the cuvette.

STEP 3. Using the appropriately labeled pipette, add 1.0 mL of substrate from the bottle of substrate to the cuvette with the buffer. Gently mix the materials in the blank by flicking the cuvette.

STEP 4. Add five (5) drops of water from the dropper bottle into the blank.

STEP 5. Dispense 3 mL of NaOH solution into the blank. *With a flat hand, gently press down on the dispenser and let up only once. You will use this blank in all exercises.*

**Figure 4.2 The Spectronic 200E control panel**

**II. B. Operation of the Spectronic 200E**

The Spectronic 200E can detect wavelengths from 340 to 1000nm. The readout can be adjusted to measure the percent (%) transmittance or absorbance. Absorbance at 410nm will be used to detect product formation in this lab.

STEP 1. Locate the power switch at the back of the Spectronic 200E and make sure it is turned on. Then press enter (↵).

STEP 2. Refer to Figure 4.2 above. On the keypad, use the up and down arrows to select Application. The menu item selected is highlighted in green. Use the right arrow to select Live Display as the type of application. The following is selected: Application: Live Display.

STEP 3. In a similar fashion, use the keyboard arrows to select Measurement Mode: absorbance.

STEP 4. Use either the keypad or the wavelength knob to set the wavelength ($\lambda$) to 410 nm.

STEP 5. Use the down arrow key to select "GO" and use the enter key (←) to start the live display.

STEP 6. Clean the blank that you prepared in Activity II.A of extraneous fingerprints by holding the cuvette at the top edge and wiping it downward with a Kimwipe.

STEP 7. Place the blank into the sample holder, gently lower the lid, and press the "Auto Zero" key (0.00). *The lid will not close all the way.* Wait until the screen displays the message "Performing Auto Zero", showing an absorbance reading of 0.00. The display will indicate in red, "Press (←) to freeze display." It is not necessary to hit the enter key at this time.

STEP 8. Clean your reaction cuvette from Activity I of extraneous fingerprints by holding the cuvette at the top edge and wiping it downward with a Kimwipe. Remove the blank, and place your reaction cuvette into the sample holder. *Please gently close the lid.* Press the green enter key (←) to initiate measurement of your sample.

   3. Record the absorbance value from the reaction cuvette here.

0.15

   4. What is the substance in the reaction cuvette that is absorbing light?

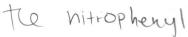
The nitrophenyl

STEP 9. Empty the reaction sample in your "R" cuvette into the hazardous waste container on the instructor's bench, rinse using the water in the water bottle provided at the instructor's bench, and empty the rinse water also into the hazardous waste container. *Do not discard the blank.*

STEP 10. To complete washing the cuvette, take it to the sink on the side counter, wash the cuvette with soap using a brush at the sink, and rinse it thoroughly with DI water.

## III. FACTORS THAT AFFECT ENZYMATIC PRODUCT FORMATION

In this activity, you will run several experiments using the same substrate and enzyme to determine how various factors affect enzymatic product formation. You will use the spectrophotometer to quantitatively measure product formation in these enzymatic reactions. Plotting your results, you will be able to easily visualize how these differing factors affect enzymatic product formation.

### III. A. The effect of enzyme concentration on product formation

In this first experiment you will explore whether adding more enzyme will make a difference to the rate of the reaction.

All your experiments will be run for the same duration of time. To do this, you will add a substance in order to stop the reaction at the predetermined time. You will stop the reaction by adding a strong base, NaOH, which will **denature** the enzyme. Denaturation refers to the destruction of the shape of the enzyme and its active site (see Figure 4.1). This will hinder the binding of substrate to the enzyme and prevent the formation of more product. Denaturation occurs under extreme conditions of pH, salt concentration and temperature.

**Materials**
> on side counter
>> - eye protection

> on your lab bench
>> bottle with buffer solution at pH 10
>> bottle with substrate (para-nitrophenyl phosphate)
>> pipettes labeled for each component above
>> dispenser pump bottle with sodium hydroxide (NaOH)
>> dropper bottle with water
>> dropper bottle with enzyme (alkaline phosphatase)
>> cuvettes in test tube rack
>> blank cuvette from Activity II.A
>> wax pencil
>> stopwatch

> on instructor's bench
>> hazardous waste container
>> bottle of distilled water

**Procedure**
STEP 1. LABEL your cuvettes 1 to 5 with the wax pencil.

STEP 2. Using the appropriately labeled pipette, transfer 1.0 mL of the pH 10 buffer solution to each of the five (5) cuvettes.

STEP 3. Using the appropriately labeled pipette, transfer 1.0 mL of the substrate solution into each of the five (5) cuvettes. Each cuvette now contains 2 mL of liquid.

STEP 4. Refer to Table 4.2 below to learn how many drops of water to add to each test cuvette. Using the dropper bottle with water, add the appropriate number of drops to each of your labeled cuvettes.

**Table 4.2 The effect of enzyme concentration on product formation**

| cuvette # | pH 10 buffer | substrate | water | enzyme | absorbance |
|-----------|--------------|-----------|---------|---------|------------|
| 1 | 1.0 mL | 1.0 mL | 4 drops | 1 drop | −0.05 |
| 2 | 1.0 mL | 1.0 mL | 3 drops | 2 drops | 0.00 |
| 3 | 1.0 mL | 1.0 mL | 2 drops | 3 drops | 0.10 |
| 4 | 1.0 mL | 1.0 mL | 1 drops | 4 drops | 0.13 |
| 5 | 1.0 mL | 1.0 mL | 0 drops | 5 drops | 0.21 |

STEP 5. Refer to Table 4.2 to learn how many drops of enzyme to add to each test cuvette. This will be a timed experiment; it is important that the reaction in each test cuvette runs exactly ten minutes (or exactly the same time period indicated by your instructor). To ensure this, you will stagger the addition of enzyme. Get your timing device ready.

5. How many drops of enzyme will be used in cuvette # 3?

3 drops

6. Why do all your experiments need to run for the same amount of time?

For consistincey

STEP 6. Note the starting time for test cuvette #1 when you add one drop of enzyme.

7. Starting time ___7:28___

STEP 7. *Stagger the addition of enzyme to* each of your five (5) cuvettes by 30-second intervals. Using the dropper bottle with enzyme, add the appropriate number of drops to each of your labeled cuvettes. Gently mix the solutions by flicking the cuvette after the addition of enzyme.

STEP 8. Wait until exactly 10 minutes after the addition of enzyme to cuvette #1, and then stop the enzymatic reaction by dispensing 3 mL of sodium hydroxide (NaOH) to cuvette #1. *With a flat hand, gently press down on the dispenser and let up only once.* Mix the solution by gently flicking the cuvette.

STEP 9. *Stagger stopping the reaction* by waiting 30 seconds before you dispense 3 mL of NaOH to cuvette #2. Wait an additional 30 seconds before you dispense NaOH to cuvette #3, and continue in the same manner for cuvettes #4 and #5. By following this procedure, all reactions should have run exactly the same time period.

STEP 10. Clean cuvette #1 with a Kimwipe and place it in the spectrophotometer and record the absorbance in Table 4.2 on the previous page. There is no need to "Auto Zero" with the blank again unless you suspect an experimental mishap.

STEP 11. Measure absorbance of the other test cuvettes using the spectrophotometer. Record your values on Table 4.2 on the previous page.

STEP 12. *In case of possible experimental mishap, keep your blank.* After recording your experimental results for III.A., discard the contents of cuvettes #1-5 into the labeled hazardous waste container on the instructor's bench. Rinse the cuvettes using the water in the water bottle provided at the instructor's bench, and empty the rinse water into the hazardous waste container.

STEP 13. Wash the cuvettes with soap using a brush at the sink on the side counter, and rinse them thoroughly with DI water.

STEP 14. Review Appendix H, preparing a simple graph. Graph your results. Include an appropriate title and label the axes. Graph paper is located at the end of the lab.

8. Which of the following was absorbing the light: substrate, enzyme or product? How do you know?

Product

9. Why did you use different amounts of enzyme in this exercise?

the difference between the concentrations

10. Why did you have to stop the reaction prior to reading absorbance?

the reaction will keep going

11. How did NaOH stop the reaction?

*The Ph dendtures it*

12. If you did not stop the reaction, when would it eventually stop?

*When the substrate is gone*

13. Which enzyme concentration caused the fastest reaction? How do you know?

*Cuvette #5, the most concentrate*

STEP 15. Have your instructor review your results and analysis before you continue.

14. Instructor initials _____

## III. B. The effect of temperature on product formation

In this experiment you will use the same substrate and enzyme to explore whether temperature will make a difference on the rate of the reaction.

**Materials**

on side counter
   eye protection
   hot water baths at 60 °C and 80 °C
   test tube holders in water baths

on your lab bench
   bottle with buffer solution at pH 10
   bottle with substrate (para-nitrophenyl phosphate)
   pipettes labeled for each component above
   dispenser pump bottle with sodium hydroxide (NaOH)
   dropper bottle with enzyme (alkaline phosphatase)
   blank from Activity II.A
   cuvettes in test tube rack
   ice chest at 4 °C  with test tube rack
   water bath at 37 °C with test tube rack
   wax pencil

on instructor's bench
> hazardous waste container
> bottle of distilled water

**Procedure**

STEP 1. Check that your labels are still visible on your cuvettes 1 to 5. If not, label with the wax pencil.

STEP 2. Refer also to Table 4.3 below. Using the appropriately labeled pipette, transfer 1.0 mL of the pH 10 buffer solution to each of the five cuvettes.

STEP 3. Refer also to Table 4.3 below. Using the appropriately labeled pipette, transfer 1.0 mL of substrate to each of the five cuvettes. Gently mix the solutions in each cuvette by flicking the cuvette.

*measure temp*

**Table 4.3 The effect of temperature on product formation**

*Ice*

| cuvette # | temp. (°C) | pH 10 buffer | substrate | enzyme | absorbance |
|-----------|------------|--------------|-----------|--------|------------|
| 1 | *blue* 4 | 1.0 mL | 1.0 mL | 5 drops | 0.05 |
| 2 | *room temp* 25 | 1.0 mL | 1.0 mL | 5 drops | 0.27 |
| 3 | *water* 37 | 1.0 mL | 1.0 mL | 5 drops | 0.24 |
| 4 | *back* 60 | 1.0 mL | 1.0 mL | 5 drops | 0.08 |
| 5 | *side* 80 | 1.0 mL | 1.0 mL | 5 drops | 0.23 |

*Sit for 10 mins, enzyme bottle add drops*

STEP 4. Refer to Table 4.3 to determine the temperature condition for each reaction cuvette. Place each cuvette in the appropriate condition as specified by the table. For example, put cuvette #1 in the ice bath at 4 °C. Allow each cuvette to acclimate for ten minutes. Keep cuvette #2 in the test tube rack for your room temperature (25 °C.) reaction. ***Each cuvette will remain in their respective conditions for the duration of the experiment.***

15. Body temperature is 98.6 °F. Which one of your cuvettes is at body temperature? (°C = 5/9 (°F-32))

*Cuvette #3*

16. How many drops of enzyme will be used in each cuvette when it is time to add the enzyme?

5 drops

STEP 5. Note the starting time for test cuvette #1 when you add enzyme.

17. Starting time ___807___

STEP 6. *Stagger the addition of enzyme* to each of your five cuvettes by 30-second intervals. Using the dropper bottle with enzyme, add five drops to each of your labeled cuvettes. Gently mix the solutions by flicking the cuvette after the addition of enzyme. ***Return each cuvette to its appropriate temperature condition.***

STEP 7. Wait until exactly 10 minutes after the addition of enzyme to cuvette #1, and then stop the enzymatic reaction by dispensing 3 mL of sodium hydroxide (NaOH) to cuvette #1. *With a flat hand, gently press down on the dispenser and let up only once.* Mix the solution by gently flicking the cuvette.

STEP 8. *Stagger stopping the reaction* by waiting 30 seconds before you dispense 3 mL of NaOH to cuvette #2. Wait an additional 30 seconds before you dispense NaOH to cuvette #3, and continue in the same manner for cuvette #4. By following this procedure, all reactions should have run exactly the same time period.

STEP 9. Clean cuvette #1 with a Kimwipe and place it in the spectrophotometer and record the absorbance in Table 4.3 on the previous page. There is no need to "Auto Zero" with the blank again unless you suspect an experimental mishap.

STEP 10. Read each of the other test cuvettes using the spectrophotometer. Record your values in Table 4.3 on the previous page.

STEP 11. After recording your values, discard the contents of the reaction cuvettes into the labeled hazardous waste container on the instructor's bench. Rinse the cuvettes using the water in the water bottle provided at the instructor's bench, and empty the rinse water into the hazardous waste container.

STEP 12. Wash the cuvettes with soap using a brush at the sink on the side counter, and rinse them thoroughly with DI water.

STEP 13. Graph your results. Include an appropriate title and label the axes. Graph paper is located at the end of this lab.

18. What was the independent variable in your experiment?

   *The independent variable is the temp*

19. Consider the absorbance readings of each reaction cuvette. Does a higher absorbance reading for a comparable experimental duration mean that the reaction rate occurred more quickly or more slowly?

   *the reaction rate was more quickly*

20. Which temperature caused the fastest reaction rate? Explain why.

   *Cuvette #2*

## III. C. The effect of pH on product formation

Changes in pH will affect the rate of enzymatic reactions. The **optimal pH** of an enzyme refers to the pH of the environment that results in the most rapid enzymatic reaction rate.

In this experiment you will determine the optimal pH for alkaline phosphatase.

**Materials**
> on side counter
>> eye protection

> on your lab bench
>> dropper bottle with buffer solution at pH 5
>> dropper bottle with buffer solution at pH 7
>> dropper bottle with buffer solution at pH 9
>> dropper bottle with buffer solution at pH 10
>> dropper bottle with buffer solution at pH 11
>> bottle with substrate (para-nitrophenyl phosphate)
>> pipette labeled for substrate
>> dropper bottle with water
>> dropper bottle with enzyme (alkaline phosphatase)
>> dispenser pump bottle with sodium hydroxide (NaOH)
>> blank from Activity II.A
>> cuvettes in test tube rack
>> wax pencil

on instructor's bench
      hazardous waste container
      bottle of distilled water

**Procedure**

STEP 1. Check that your labels are still visible on cuvettes 1 to 5. If not, label with the wax pencil.

STEP 2. Refer to Table 4.4 below to determine the correct buffer solution to add to each cuvette. At the side counter, select the appropriately labeled dropper bottle, and dispense 20 drops of the pH 5 buffer solution to reaction cuvette #1.

**Table 4.4 The effect of pH on product formation**

| cuvette # | buffer solution | substrate | enzyme | absorbance |
|-----------|-----------------|-----------|--------|------------|
| 1 | 20 drops pH 5 | 1.0 mL | 5 drops | −0.06 |
| 2 | 20 drops pH 7 | 1.0 mL | 5 drops | −0.27 |
| 3 | 20 drops pH 9 | 1.0 mL | 5 drops | −0.09 |
| 4 | 20 drops pH 10 | 1.0 mL | 5 drops | −0.16 |
| 5 | 20 drops pH 11 | 1.0 mL | 5 drops | −0.20 |

STEP 3. Using the appropriately labeled dropper bottle, dispense 20 drops of the pH 7 buffer solution to reaction cuvette #2.

STEP 4. Using the appropriately labeled dropper bottle, dispense 20 drops of the pH 9 buffer solution to reaction cuvette #3.

STEP 5. Using the appropriately labeled dropper bottle, dispense 20 drops of the pH 10 buffer solution to reaction cuvette #4.

STEP 6. Using the appropriately labeled dropper bottle, dispense 20 drops of the pH 11 buffer solution to reaction cuvette #5.

STEP 7. Using the appropriately labeled pipette, transfer 1.0 mL of the substrate solution into each of the five cuvettes. Each cuvette now contains 2 mL of liquid.

21. Why does each reaction cuvette contain the same amount of substrate and enzyme in this experiment?

*Checking for the pH*

STEP 8. This will be a timed experiment; it is important that the reaction in each test cuvette runs exactly ten minutes (or exactly the same time period indicated by your instructor). To ensure this, you will stagger the addition of enzyme. Get your timing device ready.

STEP 9. Note the starting time for test cuvette #1 when you added enzyme.

22. Starting time _____

STEP 10. *Stagger the addition of enzyme* to each of your five cuvettes by 30-second intervals. Using the dropper bottle with enzyme, add five drops to each of your labeled cuvettes. Gently mix the solutions by flicking the cuvette after the addition of enzyme.

STEP 11. Wait until exactly 10 minutes after the addition of enzyme to cuvette #1, and then stop the enzymatic reaction by dispensing 3 mL of sodium hydroxide (NaOH) to cuvette #1. *With a flat hand, gently press down on the dispenser and let up only once.* Mix the solution by gently flicking the cuvette.

STEP 12. *Stagger stopping the reaction* by waiting 30 seconds before you dispense 3 mL of NaOH to cuvette #2. Wait an additional 30 seconds before you dispense NaOH to cuvette #3, and continue in the same manner for cuvettes #4 and #5. By following this procedure, all reactions should have run exactly the same time period.

STEP 13. Clean cuvette #1 with a Kimwipe and place it in the spectrophotometer and record the absorbance in Table 4.4 on the previous page. There is no need to "Auto Zero" with the blank again unless you suspect an experimental mishap.

STEP 14. Measure absorbance of the other test cuvettes using the spectrophotometer. Record your values in Table 4.4 on the previous page.

STEP 15. After recording your experimental results, discard the contents of the cuvettes into the labeled hazardous waste container on the instructor's bench. Rinse the cuvettes using the water in the water bottle provided at the instructor's bench, and empty the rinse water into the hazardous waste container.

STEP 16. Wash the cuvettes with soap using a brush at the sink on the side counter, and thoroughly rinse them with DI water.

STEP 17. Graph your results. Include an appropriate title and label the axes. Graph paper is located at the end of this lab.

23. Explain why the following statement is false. Enzymes work only at a specific pH.

    It false because one is better than the other.

24. What is the optimal pH of this enzyme? Explain.

    Ph9

25. Discuss how the graph helps you visualize the results of this experiment.

## SUMMARY QUESTION

Identify and describe the role of the components in the enzymatic reaction you studied in today's lab. Using the results of your experiments to illustrate, explain factors that affect enzymatic reaction rates. One member of your group may be asked to share this with the class during discussion.

**POST-LAB QUESTIONS**                    Name _____

1.  Would an enzymatic reaction occur faster if you heated the substrates and enzyme? Explain your answer.

    *yes and no, yes if you heat it up too much, it will denature it*

2.  Predict what effect boiling has on the structure and active site of an enzyme? Explain.

    *will destroy the enzyme*

3.  Why can't a denatured enzyme convert substrate into product?

    *It has lost its shape so the activation site is bad*

4.  Explain why a denatured enzyme in a cell could be detrimental.

    *The reactions will not go fast enough and will die*

5.  If you did not stop the reaction, would products continue to be produced indefinitely? Explain.

    *No, it will only continue when the substrate runs out.*

6.  Cells often use the product as an inhibitor to slow or stop enzymatic activity. What is an advantage to doing so?

7.  You used 1 mL of buffer throughout today's experiments. How many liters is 1 mL?

8.  The spectrophotometer weighs 3.2 kg. How many grams is that?

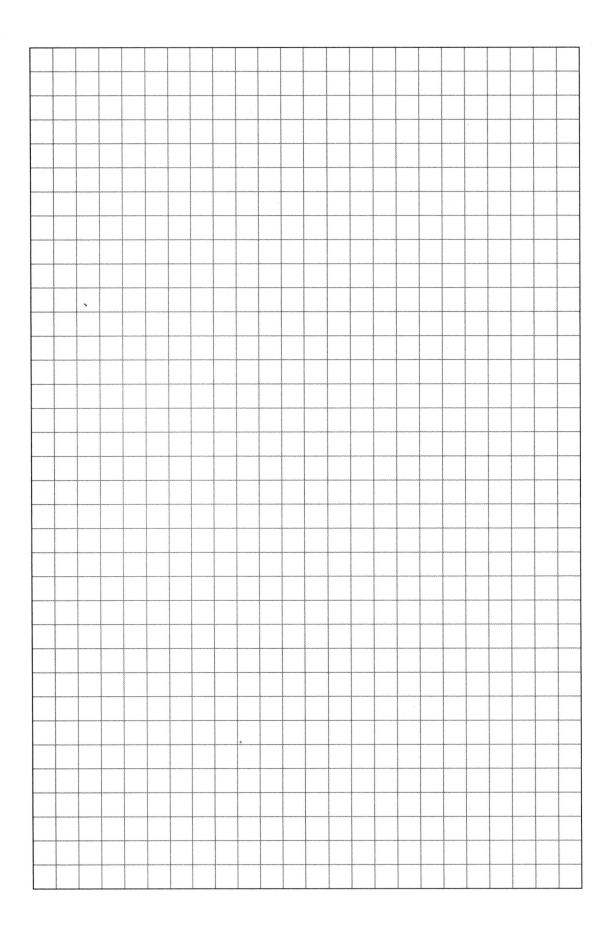

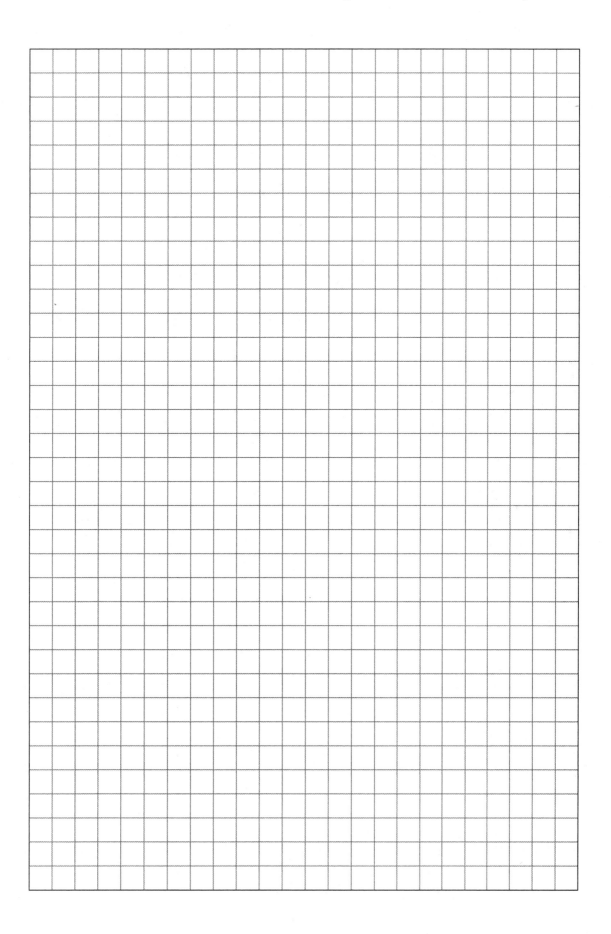

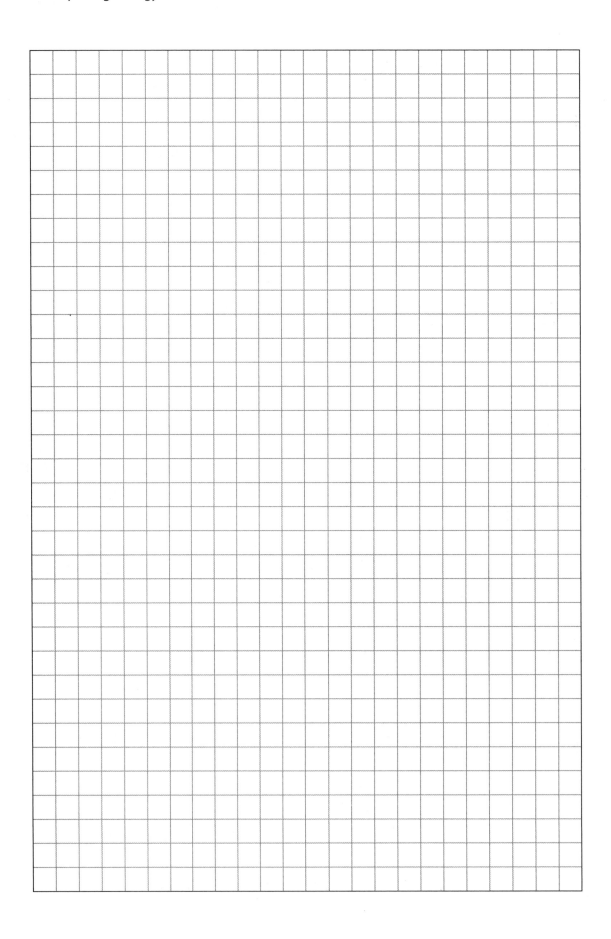

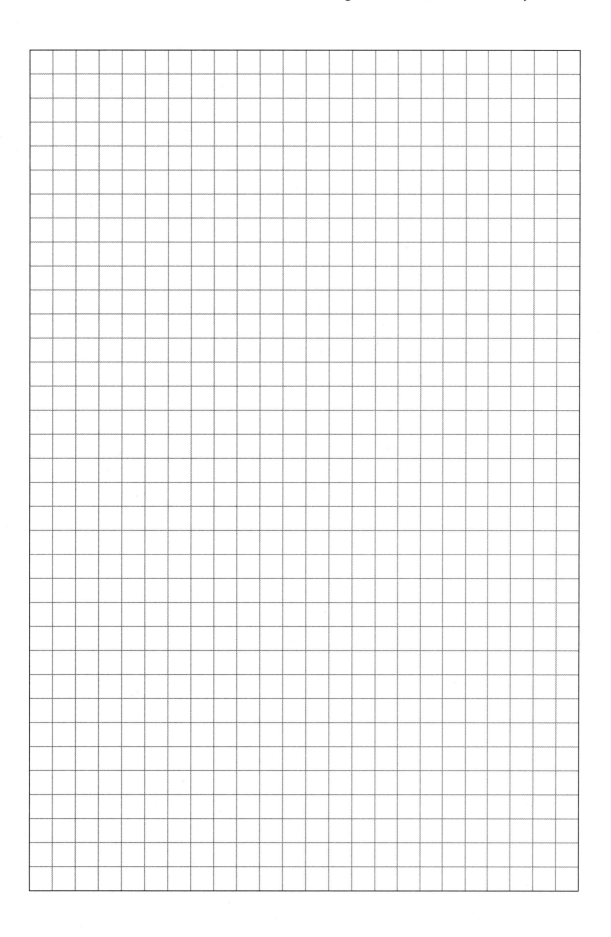

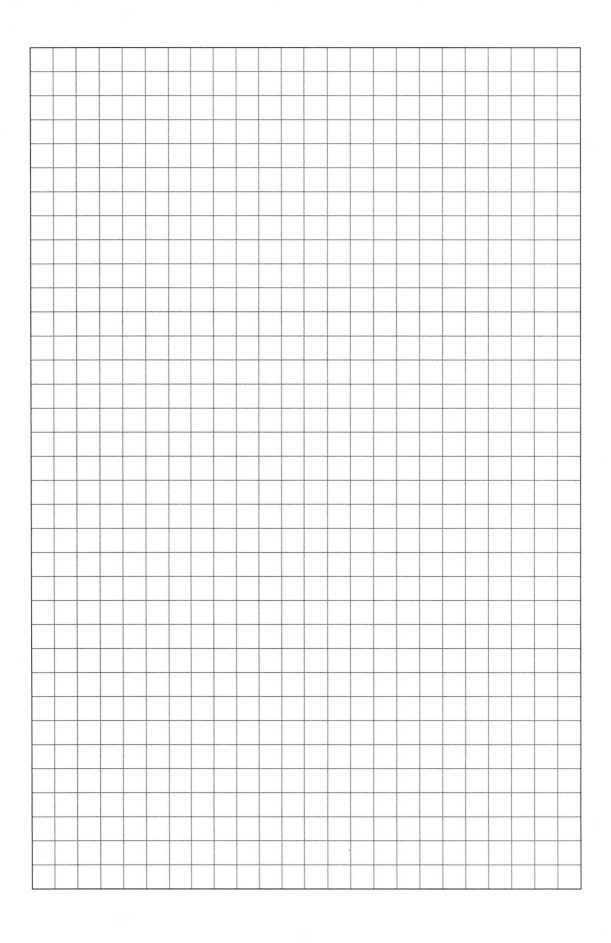

# CELLULAR METABOLISM

How do organisms get their energy? Are photosynthesis and cellular respiration related? How do plants capture light energy? Do plants and animals share similar metabolic pathways? How can we observe cellular respiration and photosynthesis in progress? How is the element carbon central to both pathways? These questions will form the framework for your activities in today's lab.

All life needs energy to survive, grow, and reproduce. How do organisms get their energy? The primary source of energy for life on earth is the sun. Plants and other photosynthetic organisms are able to capture energy from the sun using colored pigments. Plant enzymes function in a coordinated way to take water and carbon dioxide and use the captured energy of sunlight to create their food! Animals then eat the plants, and fungi and bacteria decompose plants and animals.

A **metabolic pathway** is a series of many enzymatic reactions linked together to achieve a final product. From the starting materials to the final result, we may summarize the overall metabolic reaction of **photosynthesis** as:

$$6CO_2 + 6H_2O + \text{light energy} \rightarrow C_6H_{12}O_6 + 6O_2$$

Photosynthesis produces the sugar **glucose** ($C_6H_{12}O_6$) from the raw materials of carbon dioxide ($CO_2$) and water ($H_2O$). Glucose is a reservoir of potential energy that can be torn apart for kinetic energy when the organism needs it. Some organisms split glucose in two, releasing some energy. In eukaryotes, the metabolic pathway for complete carbohydrate catabolism is called **cellular respiration**. Cellular respiration separates all the carbons in the glucose molecule in the presence of oxygen. This pathway is limited to organisms with mitochondria. The overall metabolic reaction of cellular respiration is:

$$C_6H_{12}O_6 + 6O_2 \rightarrow 6CO_2 + 6H_2O + \text{energy}$$

During cellular respiration, glucose is "burned" with oxygen and gives off carbon dioxide, water, and, most importantly, energy.

Are photosynthesis and cellular respiration related? Do they share similar pathways? Cellular respiration is much like photosynthesis in reverse. How is the element carbon central to both pathways? If you reexamine the overall equations for photosynthesis and cellular respiration, you will see the central role of carbon in both pathways. Carbon dioxide, a product of cellular respiration, is used as a substrate in photosynthesis.

**PRE-LAB QUESTIONS**                    Name _____

1.  How do different types of organisms get their energy?

2.  What is the purpose of cellular respiration?

3.  What molecules in the overall metabolic reactions for photosynthesis and cellular respiration contain carbon?

4.  What organisms do cellular respiration?

**STUDENT LEARNING OUTCOMES**

Upon completion of today's lab, you will be able to do the following:

I.   explain the methods used to study the metabolic pathways in this lab,
II.  conduct experiments to measure photosynthesis,
III. understand how plants capture light energy for photosynthesis,
IV.  conduct experiments to observe and measure cellular respiration,
V.   connect photosynthesis and cellular respiration through the carbon cycle, and
VI.  interpret results of collected data.

## I. THE METHODS USED TO STUDY METABOLIC PATHWAYS

### I. A. Interpreting chemical equations

How can we observe cellular respiration and photosynthesis in progress? Scientists use their knowledge of the overall equations for photosynthesis and cellular respiration to devise experiments to understand the processes. A scientist can follow the consumption or production of one component of the overall equation.

$$6CO_2 + 6H_2O + \text{light energy} \rightarrow C_6H_{12}O_6 + 6O_2$$

During photosynthesis, carbon dioxide and water are used to produce glucose. As proof of this process, one could look at the quantities of carbon dioxide and/or water consumed, or the amount of glucose and/or oxygen produced. Carbon dioxide is a clear and colorless gas, so it is difficult to measure it directly, but it does something in water that allows us to monitor its consumption easily.

When carbon dioxide mixes with water, it produces carbonic acid. Carbonic acid may dissociate into hydrogen ion plus bicarbonate. Carbonic acid is a weak acid because the hydrogen ion does not dissociate very easily from the bicarbonate.
This reaction is written:

$$CO_2 + H_2O \leftrightarrow H_2CO_3 \leftrightarrow H^+ + HCO_3^-$$

The free hydrogen ion ($H^+$) on the right side of the equation can be measured by using the pH meter. The pH scale is presented in Figure 5.1 on the next page.

**Figure 5.1 The pH scale**

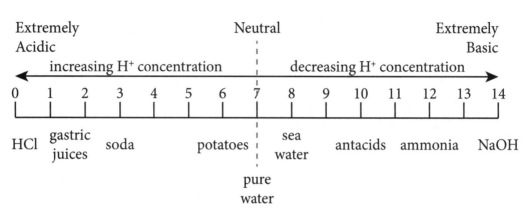

1. If the pH decreases in a solution, what does that mean about the hydrogen ion concentration?

## I. B. The indirect measurement of carbon dioxide

**Materials**

on your lab bench

two 100 mL beakers
250 mL beaker
250 mL graduated cylinder
pH meter
bottle with rinse water
rinse waste container for pH meter
drinking straw
wax pencil
Kimwipes

**Procedure**

STEP 1. Use your wax pencil to label one 100 mL beaker "hold" and one 100 mL beaker "test."

STEP 2. Take the 250 mL graduated cylinder to the sink and add at least 100 mL of tap water. Return to your lab bench.

STEP 3. Pour the tap water from the graduated cylinder into the 250 mL beaker. Turn on the pH meter, then place the pH meter into the water, stir gently, and wait a minute for the reading of the pH value to stabilize. Record the value in Table 5.1 below, under "initial pH" for both beakers.

STEP 4. Remove the pH meter, use the "rinse water" bottle to rinse the pH meter, *draining into the rinse waste container.* Put the pH meter into the rinse waste container while you complete the next step.

STEP 5. Use the 50 mL graduated cylinder to measure exactly 50 mL of the water you just tested to put into the 100 mL "hold" beaker and 50 mL of the water your just tested into the "test" beaker.

STEP 6. Remove the pH meter, use the "rinse water" bottle to rinse the pH meter, draining into the rinse waste container. Gently shake off the excess water from the pH meter and then dry the outside housing of the pH meter with a Kimwipe. *Now put the pH meter into the hold beaker and leave it there.*

### Table 5.1 pH of hold and test beakers

|  | initial pH | 30-second pH |
|---|---|---|
| hold beaker |  |  |
| test beaker |  |  |

In humans, the lungs function in **gas exchange**. Oxygen diffuses across the lungs into the bloodstream and carbon dioxide diffuses from the blood into the lungs.

STEP 7. Using a clean drinking straw, blow gently into the water of the test beaker for at least 30 seconds.

STEP 8. The pH meter has been in the hold beaker for at least 30 seconds. Record the pH value of the hold beaker under "30-second pH" in Table 5.1.

STEP 9. Remove the pH meter from the hold beaker. Use the "rinse water" bottle to rinse the pH meter, *draining into the rinse waste container.* Gently shake off the excess water from the pH meter and then dry the outside housing of the pH meter with a Kimwipe.

STEP 10. Place the pH meter into the test beaker, stir gently, and wait a minute for the reading of the pH value to stabilize. Record the value in Table 5.1 under "30-second pH" for the test beaker.

STEP 11. Remove the pH meter, use the "rinse water" bottle to rinse the pH meter, *draining into the rinse waste container*. Gently shake off the excess water from the pH meter and then dry the outside housing of the pH meter with a Kimwipe. Return your pH meter to the hold beaker.

STEP 12. Keep the hold beaker with the pH meter in it for further use. Clean the test beaker in preparation for the next activity.

2.  Explain any change in the pH reading of your test beaker.

## II. MEASURING PHOTOSYNTHESIS

In this activity, you will be using *Elodea* sp., an aquatic plant, to measure factors that influence photosynthesis. The complete equation for photosynthesis is:

$$6CO_2 + 6H_2O + \text{light energy} \rightarrow C_6H_{12}O_6 + 6O_2$$

You will have three plant chambers: one exposed to the full spectrum of light, one in darkness, and one with a filter that lets only one particular color of light through. The color options are green, red, and blue. In this experiment you will place a plant in water and look for evidence of photosynthesis by recording the pH as an indirect measure of carbon dioxide consumed.

3.  What are the two hypotheses being tested by putting the plants in different chambers?

4.  What do you expect to happen to the pH of the water in the plant chamber in light?

**Materials**

      on side counter
            *Elodea* sp.
            metric ruler
            five chambers: clear, dark, red, blue, and green
            grow lights

      on your lab bench
            50 mL graduated cylinder
            250 mL graduated cylinder
            four 250 mL beakers
            400 mL beaker tap water
            pH meter
            bottle with rinse water
            rinse waste container
            drinking straw
            wax pencil

**Procedure**

STEP 1. Use the wax pencil to LABEL your 250 mL beakers with your name and "1", "2", "3", and "4".

STEP 2. Take the 250 mL graduated cylinder to the sink to measure 200 mL of tap water. Return to your bench and the tap water to the 400 mL beaker. Use the drinking straw to blow into the tap water for 30 seconds.

STEP 3. Turn on the pH meter, then place the pH meter into the 200 mL of tap water in the 400 mL beaker, stir gently, and wait a minute for the reading of the pH value to stabilize. Record the value here and in Table 5.2 on the next page, under time 0.

       5.  Initial pH value of water _____

STEP 4. Use the 50 mL graduated cylinder to measure exactly 50 mL of the water you just tested to put into each of your four 250 mL test beakers.

STEP 5. At the side counter, locate the water plant, *Elodea* sp. *Select springs of similar appearance for your experiment.* Measure out three sets of 24 cm of sprigs, for a total of 72 cm of the water plant. Return to your bench and add 24 cm of *Elodea* sp. to each of the 250 mL test beakers labeled 2, 3 and 4.

STEP 6. The instructor will assign the chamber colors (green, red, or blue) for each lab bench. Record your assigned color on Table 5.2 on the next page.

**Table 5.2  pH of water in beakers 1-4**

| beaker number | conditions | time 0 pH<br><br>Start: | time 90 minutes pH<br><br>Finish: |
|---|---|---|---|
| 1 | clear cover, no plant | | |
| 2 | clear cover, with plant | | |
| 3 | foil cover, with plant | | |
| 4 | color:_____ with plant | | |

6. Why do chambers 2, 3, and 4 need the same 24 cm of plant material?

7. Explain how you can look for evidence of photosynthesis by measuring changes in pH.

8. What is the purpose of the chamber with no plant?

STEP 7. Place each of your four test beakers containing plant material in the appropriate chamber on the side counter. Record the start time in Table 5.2 above. Wait 90 minutes. *You may proceed with the next lab activities during the waiting period.*

STEP 8. After 90 minutes, pick up the test beakers from the chambers, return to your lab bench, and immediately measure the pH of each beaker. *Be sure to rinse, shake and dry the outside housing of the pH meter with a Kimwipe before each new measurement.* Record your values at 90 minutes in Table 5.2 on the previous page.

9.  What are the colors of light that your colored chamber allowed through to the plant in beaker 4?

10. Did your plant photosynthesize while under your chamber? What evidence do you have to support your claim?

11. Wavelengths of light are measured in nm. How many cm is 450 nm?

STEP 9. Complete Table 5.3 below with the class averages for each condition.

**Table 5.3  Class averages of the pH in beaker water under different conditions**

| conditions | time 0 pH | time 60 minutes pH |
|---|---|---|
| green cover, with plant | | |
| blue cover, with plant | | |
| red cover, with plant | | |

12. Compare your data to the class data with other colored chambers. Did every experimental condition have similar results? Explain.

## III. CAPTURING LIGHT USED IN PHOTOSYNTHESIS

### III. A. Light and the electromagnetic spectrum

Our eyes can detect a portion of the electromagnetic spectrum with **wavelengths** of energy ranging from about 400 to 700 **nanometers** (1 nm = 1/1,000,000 meter). Wavelength is the distance between two crests of the waves. Shorter waves have higher energy; think about them as coming at you faster. We see different wavelengths of light as different **colors**.

**Materials**

> on side counter
>> chart of electromagnetic spectrum

**Procedure**

Go to side counter to observe the chart of the electromagnetic spectrum. Appendix E identifies the wavelengths of colors in the visible spectrum.

13.  Energy coming towards you in waves 450nm in length would appear to your eyes as what color?

14.  What color would you perceive if the wavelength was 650nm?

15.  Why would you not be able to see a wave 1000nm long?

All materials contain **pigments** that **absorb**, **reflect** and/or **transmit** light. Your red shirt, for instance, reflects red. We see the red light because the wavelength associated with red is neither transmitted (passed through) or absorbed, but is reflected back towards our eyes.

16.  A leaf transmits some light energy and the rest is either absorbed and used in photosynthesis or reflected off the leaf's surface. What color is reflected the most?

### III. B. Identifying the energy wavelengths used by plants

**Materials**

> on side counter
>> spectroscope
>> test tube with plant extract

A **spectroscope** is a device that disperses light into multiple wavelengths, permitting you to see each color of light distinctly.

**Procedure**

STEP 1. Obtain a spectroscope and make sure the slit at the far end is open. Look through the round opening and point the spectroscope at a light source, preferably outside in the daylight. Record the order of the colors you see in the first column of Table 5.4 below.

**Table 5.4  Colors observed through the spectroscope**

| colors visible in direct full light | colors visible through plant extract |
|---|---|
|  |  |
|  |  |
|  |  |
|  |  |
|  |  |
|  |  |
|  |  |

The lab technician has chemically extracted the light harvesting **photosynthetic pigments** from spinach leaves.

STEP 2. Place a small vial of pigment extract between the spectroscope and the light source and record the colors you see in the second column of Table 5.4 above. Any colors no longer visible are those that are absorbed by the chloroplasts.

17.  What colors are no longer visible?

## III. C. Separation of plant pigments

There are a variety of pigments within a chloroplast. The most important and abundant photosynthetic pigment is **chlorophyll a**, which absorbs blue and red wavelengths and reflects blue-green. Chlorophyll a has the visual appearance of blue-green. The other pigments found in plants are called accessory pigments because they pass light energy they trap to chlorophyll a. **Chlorophyll b** is yellow-green. Other accessory pigments include carotenes, phycoerythrins, and phycocyanins. They are usually present in such small quantities that they are masked by the abundance of chlorophyll. The various photosynthetic pigments have different molar masses.

18. Do heavier molecules diffuse more slowly or more quickly when compared to lighter weight molecules?

In the following activity you will use **chromatography** to separate plant pigments. This will be done by transferring plant pigments from a leaf onto paper. When the paper is placed in liquid the pigments will diffuse up the paper with the liquid.

19. What do you predict will happen as the different photosynthetic pigments diffuse?

### Materials
on side counter
> chromatography paper strips
> chromatography solvent
> a penny
> a leaf or two of spinach or other plant
> poster of the absorbance spectra of various plant pigments
> chart of the absorbance spectra of chlorophyll a, chlorophyll b, and other plant pigments
> small metric ruler

on your lab bench
> test tube rack with large test tube and stopper apparatus to be used as the chromatography chamber

on instructor's bench
> chromotography waste container

**Procedure**

STEP 1. Take the chromatography chamber at your lab bench to the side counter. Obtain a chromatography paper strip, and fold the chromatography paper approximately 1 cm to fit into the clip of the stopper of the chromatography chamber. With a proper fit the paper will lie flat without buckling when the chamber is closed.

STEP 2. Lay a spinach leaf across the pencil mark of your chromatography strip and roll the edge of a penny back and forth across the spinach on the line until you have transferred a solid green stain onto the chromatography paper 1 cm from the end.

STEP 3. Pour just enough of the chromatography solvent into the chromatography chamber to cover the tip of your paper strip when the paper strip is in the test tube, but not enough solvent to reach the green stain. The height of the solvent will be less than 1 cm.

STEP 4. Carefully insert the paper strip back in the clip of the stopper, place the stopper into the chromatography chamber, and allow the chromatography solvent to diffuse upwards for approximately 15 minutes until the diffusion line is just below the clip.

STEP 5. As soon as the solvent reaches the clip, remove the paper strip, lay it on your bench, and let it dry. Discard the used chromatography solvent from your chamber into the labeled waste container on the instructor's bench.

STEP 6. Tape or DRAW your results below before the colors fade.

20.  LABEL the blue-green chlorophyll a and the yellow-green chlorophyll b. Which chlorophyll molecule is heavier? Explain your answer.

21.  How many other photosynthetic pigments are there?

22.  What colors are they?

STEP 7. Observe the absorbance spectra of plant pigments on the chart posted in the lab. Identify the wavelength of the peak absorbance for each plant pigment and record it in Table 5.5 below.

**Table 5.5 Wavelengths and appearance of peak absorbance for each plant pigment**

| plant pigment | peak absorbance (nm) | visual appearance |
| --- | --- | --- |
| chlorophyll a | | blue-green |
| chlorophyll b | | yellow-green |
| β-carotene | | orange |
| phycoerythrin | | red |
| phycocyanin | | blue |

23.  Why do plants have more than one pigment?

24. Do you think the plants under the green, red, or blue filter will have the least amount of photosynthetic activity? Explain your answer.

## IV. CELLULAR RESPIRATION

$$C_6H_{12}O_6 + 6O_2 \rightarrow 6CO_2 + 6H_2O + energy$$

During the metabolic process of cellular respiration, carbon dioxide is produced. In the next activity, you will see evidence of the metabolism of glucose by the production of carbon dioxide.

25. When more carbon dioxide is produced, what will happen to the pH of an aqueous solution? Explain your answer.

**Measuring cellular respiration in fish**

**Materials**
    on side counter
        room temperature pond water (in labeled carboy)
        fish in aquarium
        fish net
        250 mL waste beaker

    on your lab bench
        50 mL graduated cylinder
        100 mL beaker
        pH meter
        bottle with rinse water
        waste beaker
        magnifying glass
        Kimwipes

**Procedure**
STEP 1. Using the graduated cylinder, measure 50 mL of room-temperature pond water and pour it into a 100 mL beaker to prepare a pond for your fish.

STEP 2. Use the pH meter to measure the pH and record your starting pH reading in Table 6.6 on the next page.

STEP 3. Carry your pond over to the small fish aquarium on the side counter. Use a net to catch one or two fish from the aquarium and *carefully* transfer them to your pond by lowering the net into the beaker.

STEP 4. Let the fish acclimate for five minutes. Refer to Figure 5.2 below, fish with operculum and gills labeled. Observe the fish opening its mouth and the **operculum (1)**, the protective flap that covers the **gills** (2). Use the magnifying glass. The fish are moving water that is gulped into their mouths over their gills in order to extract oxygen from the water.

**Figure 5.2 Fish with operculum and gills labeled**

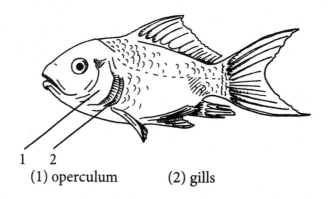

1   2
(1) operculum          (2) gills

26.   What structure is used by fish to get rid of carbon dioxide?

27.   What general process drives gas exchange at the cellular level?

STEP 5. Note the time and use the pH meter to measure the pH of the water in your fish pond again at 15 and 30 minutes. Rinse your pH meter, shake off the excess water, and dry the outside of the housing with a Kimwipe before each measurement, and return it to the hold beaker between measurements.

**Table 5.6 Pond water pH with small fish over time**

| time (min) | 0 | 15 | 30 |
|---|---|---|---|
| pH | | | |

28.  State the hypothesis of the experiment.

STEP 6. Carry your pond with your fish over to the small fish aquarium. Use the net to catch your fish while pouring your used pond water into a 250-mL waste beaker by the small fish aquarium. Return the fish to the small fish aquarium. *Do not add the wastewater to the fish aquarium*, but rather DISCARD THE WASTEWATER DOWN THE SINK.

## V. THE CARBON CYCLE/ Connecting photosynthesis and cellular respiration

The Earth may be divided into four component spheres: the atmosphere, the hydrosphere, the lithosphere, and the biosphere. The atmosphere is composed of the parts of the planet with vapor or gases. The hydrosphere is composed of the parts of the planet with water, and the lithosphere is composed of the parts of the planet that contain rocks and sediments. The biosphere is composed of the parts of the planet that contain life.

Carbon and carbon based molecules are found in all four spheres. The atmosphere includes carbon in the form of the gases carbon dioxide ($CO_2$) and methane ($CH_4$). These two gases affect the temperature of the Earth by reflecting heat back to the surface. In the hydrosphere, carbon dioxide dissolves in water, reaching an equilibrium with carbon dioxide in the atmosphere. This slows the rate of warming caused by carbon dioxide, but also changes the chemistry of the planet's waters. Carbon is also found as methane hydrates, a crystalline solid that consists of a methane molecule surrounded by a cage of interlocking water molecules, on the sea floor. The lithosphere includes carbon reservoirs as natural gas, oils, methane hydrates, and solid rock. Carbon may be released from reservoirs through combustion or by the natural eruption of gases in volcanoes. Methane hydrates are sensitive sediments that can rapidly dissociate with an increase in temperature or a decrease in pressure. In the biosphere, carbon is stored in organisms. Forests play a significant role in carbon storage. In this lab you have explored how carbon dioxide is used and produced by organisms of the biosphere.

**Procedure**

Study Figure 5.3 below, the chart of the four component spheres, and Figure 5.4 on the next page, the carbon cycle, before answering the questions.

**Figure 5.3 The component spheres of the Earth**

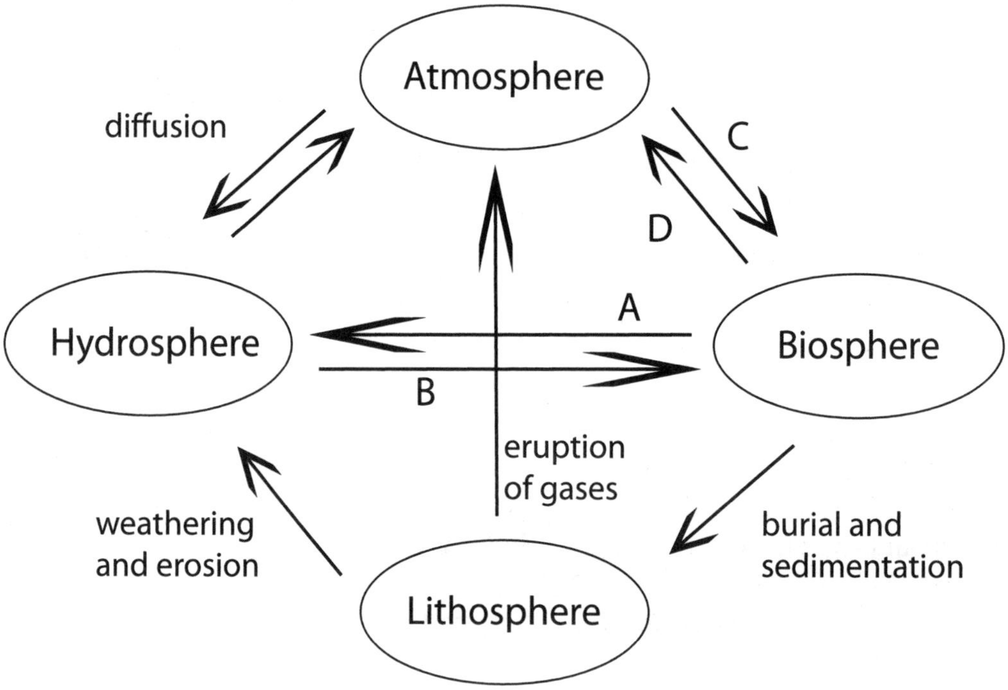

29. Match the letter on the figure with the description of the process.

_____ acquisition of carbon dioxide for photosynthesis

_____ acquisition of water for photosynthesis

_____ release of carbon dioxide as product of respiration

_____ release of water as product of respiration

**Figure 5.4 The carbon cycle**

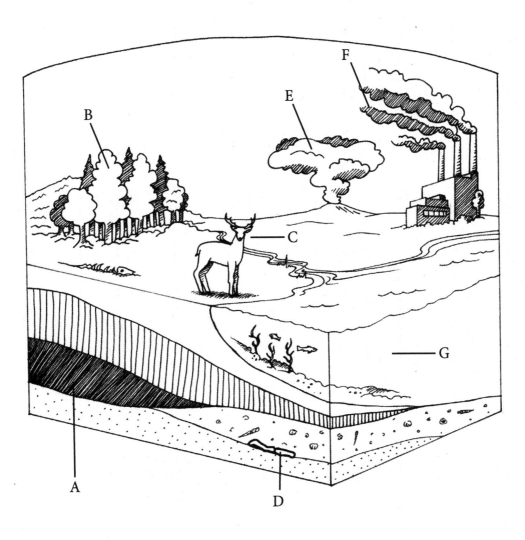

30. Match the letters on the figure with the components of the carbon cycle.

_____ burning of fossil fuels

_____ cellular respiration

_____ dissolved carbon dioxide

_____ fossil fuel reservoir

_____ methane hydrates

_____ photosynthesis

_____ volcanic release of carbon dioxide

31. What process(es) remove(s) carbon from the atmosphere?

32. What process(es) release(s) carbon to the atmosphere?

33. Predict what happens to global atmospheric carbon when forests are destroyed.

34. In the introduction to this section, it was stated that carbon dioxide could alter the chemistry of the planet's water. Explain how.

35. Methane hydrates on the sea floor may be released as the climate warms. Explain how this could further impact atmospheric temperatures.

36. How are cellular respiration and photosynthesis related to the carbon cycle?

**SUMMARY QUESTION**

Relate what happened to the pH in the fish pond and pH in the water with *Elodea* due to carbon dioxide use or production. Include in your answer support from the equations for cellular respiration and photosynthesis. One member of your group may be asked to share this with the class during discussion.

**POST-LAB QUESTIONS**                    **Name** _____

1. What indirect measurement did you use in this lab? Why was this necessary?

2. What is the difference in the hydrogen ion concentration in a solution with a pH of 5 and a solution with a pH of 8?

3. What role do plants play in the carbon cycle?

4. Throughout history, data shows the levels of atmospheric $CO_2$ have fluctuated. What are some concerns about the rising $CO_2$ levels in the global atmosphere?

5. How would an increase in the level of dissolved carbon dioxide in the ocean lead to the acidification of the ocean?

6. If carbon dioxide from cellular respiration leads to an increase in free hydrogen ions in solution, then how do animals keep from dying from acidosis?

*Questions continue on the next page.*

7. You added 75 mL into each beaker. How many liters is 75 mL?

8. Like you, some animals regulate their body temperature by adjusting their metabolic rate. These animals are considered **endothermic**. Maintaining a steady temperature requires careful regulation and active metabolism to generate heat. Another strategy is to permit the body's temperature to fluctuate with the environment; these animals are called ectotherms. Being ectothermic reduces the amount of food required for survival. Fish are **ectothermic**, and their metabolic rate changes as their temperature changes. What do you predict would happen to the metabolic rate of fish if the temperature in the aquarium drops? Explain your answer.

# THE CELL CYCLE

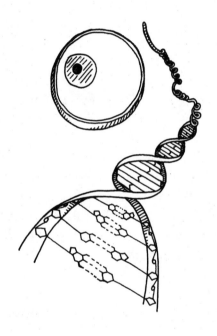

What does the cell do every day? How are decisions made about its activities? Where is the DNA, what does it look like, and what's behind its use? How does the cell make proteins? These questions will form the framework for your activities in today's lab.

What does the cell do every day? How are decisions made about its activities? As the fundamental unit of the body, the cell is responsible for carrying out the activities necessary for life, such as obtaining energy and making the products it needs. Cells may also replicate themselves for tissue repair or for growth. The cell cycles from the procedures of completing daily tasks to replicating itself. Fundamental to all activities as the cell cycles is the molecule, deoxyribonucleic acid (**DNA**). Cell replication is very exciting for biologists so they named the different phases of the cell cycle in reference to when the cell was replicating. When not dividing, the cell is said to be in **interphase**. During interphase, DNA is controlling all the everyday activities of the cell. The time when the cell divides into two is called **cytokinesis**. Before the cell can divide, however, it needs to copy all the material it has, especially its DNA, and then sort it. DNA and other component replication happen in interphase, but the sorting process happens later. **Mitosis** is the special phase of the cell cycle when the replicated DNA is sorted and separated. Mitosis is further divided into four steps: **prophase**, **metaphase**, **anaphase**, and **telophase**. In the first activity, you will learn to recognize a cell in interphase, and the four phases of mitosis by observing two types of eukaryotic cells.

Where is the DNA, what does it look like, and what's behind its use? All life on Earth has DNA, and the DNA molecule operates in a similar fashion in all life. DNA directs the production of proteins, which form the basis of cell structures and **enzymes**, molecules that enhance metabolic activities. How does it do this? DNA is built in a series of units called nucleotides. Each nucleotide has a sugar molecule (deoxyribose), a phosphate group, and a nitrogenous base, sometimes simply referred to as a "base." Strings of nucleotides make up two strands in a DNA molecule. The bases of each strand are oriented to bind with bases of the other strand while the sugar and phosphate molecules form the backbones of the strands. The sequence of the bases is different in each species and is essential to the role of DNA.

There are strict **base-pairing rules** that guide both the replication of DNA and the use of DNA to make proteins. The bases of the nucleotides in the DNA strands form hydrogen bonds based upon their chemical structures. Adenine (A) always binds with thymine (T), and cytosine (C) always binds with guanine (G). The rules are so reliable that if you have one side of the DNA strand, you can determine the bases on the other side. This is referred to as **complementary base pairing**. In the second activity of today's lab, you will build a small segment of DNA given a sequence of bases, and then replicate it in preparation for cell division.

**PRE-LAB QUESTIONS**                    Name _____

1.  When a cell is not actively dividing, what phase is it in?

2.  What phase of the cell cycle do prophase, metaphase, anaphase, and telophase collectively make up? What happens in this phase?

3.  What is meant by base-pairing rules, and what are the base pairing rules for DNA?

## STUDENT LEARNING OUTCOMES

Upon completion of today's lab, you will be able to do the following:

    I.   describe the stages of the cell cycle,
    II.  isolate DNA,
    III. use the base pairing rules for making DNA, and
    IV. explain the processes of protein synthesis.

## I. OBSERVING THE PHASES OF THE CELL CYCLE

In this activity, you will learn to recognize the phases of the cell cycle in eukaryotic species. DNA in eukaryotes is located in strands associated with proteins, together called **chromatin**. Chromatin condenses into visible **chromosomes** for cell replication. The cell more easily manages chromosomes than the diffuse chromatin. During prophase and metaphase, the chromosomes look like an "x" because the replicated copy remains attached to the original strand of DNA at a position called the **centromere**. The replicates are called "sisters" and contain identical information.

In multicellular eukaryotes, cells are found organized by function and structure into tissues. To best view all phases of the cell cycle, we have selected fast-growing tissues: embryonic animal tissue and a plant root tip. The embryonic animal tissue is from a whitefish blastula, and the plant tissue comes from the onion, *Allium* sp.

### Materials
    on side counter
        charts and models of the cell cycle

    on your lab bench
        hand clicker counter
        prepared slides:
        *Allium* sp. (onion) root tip
        whitefish blastula (animal)

### Procedure
STEP 1. Observe the charts and models of the cell cycle on display on the side counter, depicting interphase, and all the phases of mitosis and cytokinesis.

    1.  Identify the correct phase by labeling Figure 6.1 on the next page with the correct name of the phase.

**Figure 6.1 The cell cycle**

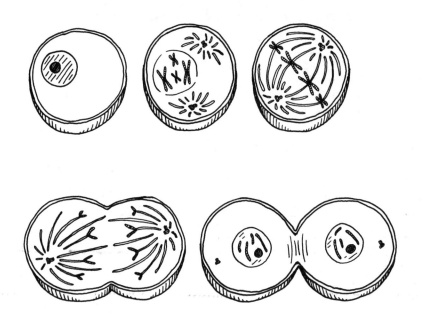

STEP 2. Obtain a slide of the onion (*Allium* sp.) root tip and focus it at the magnification on your microscope where you can identify the phases of the cell cycle in the cells. The area of cell division is found just above the root cap at the rounded tip of the root.

2. Which objective lens do you select when first viewing a specimen? What magnification will that be when first viewing a specimen?

4

Cells spend most of their time in interphase doing everyday activities, but in the rapidly growing root tip, you will see many cells in the different phases of mitosis. The slide is a snapshot of root tip growth. The time a cell spends in each phase is represented by the percentage of cells in that phase in your field.

STEP 3. Use the 10X objective lens to view the slide at a total of 100 X magnification. Using the hand clicker counter, count the number of cells in each phase within your field of view.

3. Record the number of cells you located in each phase of mitosis in Table 6.1 on the next page.

**Table 6.1  Number of cells identified in each phase of mitosis**

|  | number of cells |
|---|---|
| prophase | 36 |
| metaphase | 9 |
| anaphase | 1 |
| telophase | 1 |

4. Which is the shortest phase of mitosis? Which is the longest phase of mitosis? Does this make sense to you? Explain why or why not.

Anaphase is the shortest phase of mitosis.
Prophase is the longest phase of mitosis

in anaphase the sister chromatids are pulled apart to opposite ends of the cell.

STEP 4. Obtain a slide of the whitefish blastula, place it on the microscope, and focus it at the best magnification to view the cells in division.

5. What differences do you see between these cells and the onion root tip cells?

the onion root cells are rectangle, the
animal cell - fish is circular cells.

STEP 5. Locate one of the whitefish blastula cells undergoing mitosis, and place the pointer on it.

6. What phase of mitosis is showing?

prophase

7. Have your instructor verify and initial your lab book here. _____

8. Is there DNA in the cell during the entire cell cycle? Explain your answer.

yes dna is in the entire cell cycle

## II. ISOLATION OF DNA

As we have come to learn, DNA is found in all living organisms. In this activity, you will isolate DNA from strawberries. Chromosomes containing the DNA are located in the nucleus of the eukaryotic strawberry. In order to isolate DNA from the nucleus, you will break open the cells of a strawberry, prepare a filtered extract containing strawberry DNA, and then separate the DNA molecules from the remaining cell parts.

9. Given the information that you've learned about DNA, hypothesize what DNA will look like when extracted from plant cells.

### Materials
on side counter
>        resealable bag (6" x 9")
>        coffee filter, cone-shaped, #2 size
>        150-mL beaker
>        disposable plastic pipette
>        strawberry
>        extraction buffer
>        10 mL graduated cylinder
>        cold ethanol in a test tube found in ice chest
>        hooked glass pipette

on instructor's bench
>        waste container for ethanol extract

### II. A. DNA extraction

**Procedure**

STEP 1. Locate the materials you need on the side counter. Remove the stem and leaves from a strawberry and place it in a resealable bag (press the air out and seal it).

STEP 2. Gently mash the bagged strawberry with your fist and fingers for 2 minutes.

STEP 3. Open the bag and add 10 mL of extraction buffer to the bag (press the air out carefully and seal the bag).

STEP 4. Mash the bagged strawberry again for one minute.

STEP 5. Drape the coffee filter over the beaker (make sure that the bottom the filter does not touch the bottom of the beaker).

STEP 6. Pour the mashed strawberries with extraction buffer into the filter and let drip into the beaker (this will take approximately 10 minutes).

STEP 7. As you wait for the solution to filter, *answer the following questions*:

10.  What was the purpose of mashing up the strawberry?

*to collect dna*

11.  What does the extraction buffer do? (Hint: extraction buffer contains soap. What does soap do when you wash your hands?)

*It breaks down the lipid.*

12.  What does the filter do?

*keep the chunks of strawberries out*

## II. B. DNA isolation

### Procedure
STEP 1. After your liquid filtrate has filtered through, obtain one test tube with ice-cold ethanol.

STEP 2. Read STEPS 3-5 carefully before continuing.

STEP 3. Using a pipette, remove some of the strawberry extract from the beaker and carefully pipet the extract into the alcohol in the test tube and watch the solution precipitate (you should see a visible change from an all liquid solution to one in which a solid and liquid separate from one another). *Do not shake the tube!*

STEP 4. Very gently swirl the tube once or twice then let the tube remain undisturbed for a few minutes.

STEP 5. Watch the interface (where the alcohol and extract come into contact with each other). Keep the tube at eye level so you can see what's happening.

13. What do you see appearing?

*a white film or almost cotton candy film.*

STEP 6. Use a hooked pipette to pull out the substance that you see at the interface so that you may better describe what you observe.

14. DRAW what you see and note any other observations.

15. Since strawberries were once living, and we extracted DNA from them, what does this mean about the foods we eat?

*Everything you eat has DNA in it.*

STEP 7. Discard the ethanol extraction into the designated waste container on the instructor's bench. Put the empty test tube in the adjacent test tube rack. Dispose of the filter and resealable bag into the trash. Clean all other used glassware and return it to the side counter.

## III. BUILDING DNA USING DNA BASE-PAIRING RULES

When isolated from a cell and stretched out and magnified, the DNA of chromatin strands looks like a twisted ladder. This shape is called a double helix. Strings of nucleotides form the two strands of the DNA molecule, analogous to the sides of the ladder. The bases between the strands form hydrogen bonds with each other, like the steps on the ladder. There are four types of chemical bases in DNA: adenine (A), cytosine (C), guanine (G), and thymine (T). They form pairs in very specific ways: adenine (A) always pairs with thymine (T) and cytosine (C) always pairs with guanine (G). See Figures 6.2 and 6.3 on the next page.

## Figure 6.2 The structure of DNA

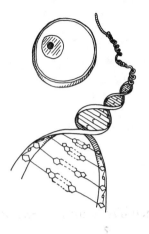

## Figure 6.3 A nucleotide

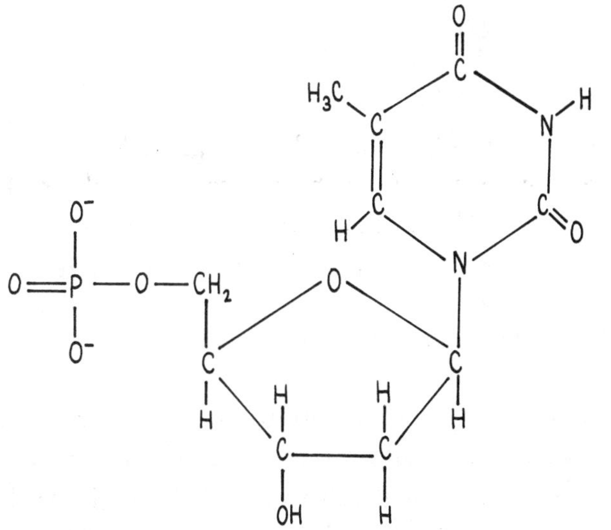

**Materials**

> containers with white, red, yellow, orange, blue, and green beads
> plastic connectors

**Procedure**

STEP 1. Your task is to use the following materials and procedure to construct a model of DNA. Assemble the four types of nucleotides (colored beads) to be used in your DNA model from the beads found in containers on your lab bench. The model nucleotides are comprised of three beads to represent the three components: the sugar deoxyribose (white), a phosphate group (red), and a nitrogen base (use the key provided to determine which bead color corresponds to which nitrogen base). You will need to make up 20 thymine, 20 adenine, 22 cytosine, and 22 guanine nucleotides. Refer to Figure 6.4 on the next page for the proper assembly of the beads.

**Figure 6.4 Assemby of nucleotide and DNA using beads**

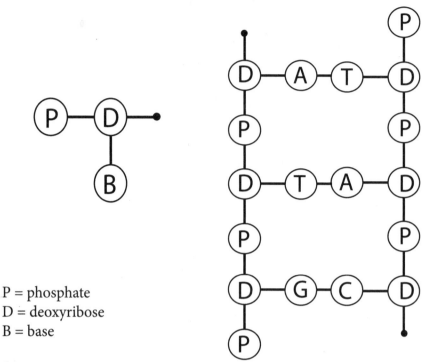

P = phosphate
D = deoxyribose
B = base

Bead colors:

| | | |
|---|---|---|
| adenine = yellow | thymine = orange | phosphate = red |
| guanine = green | cytosine = blue | deoxyribose = white |

Since the bases pair with each other, the number of base pairs can be used to measure the length of the DNA. The total number of base pairs varies depending on the species; humans have about three billion base pairs in their chromosomes! You will work with only a tiny fragment of a chromosome.

STEP 2. Given the sequence below of bases on one side of a piece of DNA molecule, write below them the bases of the complementary side.

16. T A C C T A G C G C A C A T G T A G G T G

A T G G A T C G C G T G T A C A T C C A C

STEP 3. Using the sequence above as a guide, assemble your DNA molecule keeping in mind that the sides of the DNA ladder is made of alternating sugar and phosphate groups. Place the colored bead for the complementary chemical bases adjacent to each other and connect with the small plastic bead connectors to simulate hydrogen bonds. Carefully twist your DNA molecule so that it looks like a double helix.

STEP 4. Set your model down on a blank sheet of paper. LABEL one of each of the following: adenine, thymine, cytosine, guanine, deoxyribose, and phosphate.

17. Show your finished and labeled model to your instructor before continuing on. Your instructor will initial your lab book here to verify the completion of your DNA molecule.

_____

All the components of a cell are replicated in preparation for cell division. You will simulate DNA replication with your model.

18. What are the component units that make up the DNA molecule?

nucleotides are sugar, phosphate

DNA is replicated in a process called **semi-conservative replication**. Semi-conservative replication will result in half of the original molecule of DNA becoming part of each new copy.

STEP 5. Separate your DNA molecule into two strands by breaking the hydrogen bond connections between the bases.

19. Which components of DNA make up the sides of the "ladder"?

Sugar and phosphate

STEP 6. Continue with the replication process by assembling the new sides of each DNA molecule.

20. How are your two strands of DNA related to each other?

nucleotides have to Match up; they are copies

21. Why is it important that a complete copy of the entire DNA is replicated during interphase?

S phase of interphase, the Dna is copied.

★ Both cells have DNA.

STEP 7. Separate and return the beads and plastic connectors to their respective containers.

## IV. MAKING A PROTEIN

How does the cell make proteins? DNA is responsible for the direction of cellular activities by coding for the production of proteins used in building structures and helping metabolism. The portion of DNA that is used as a code to make a particular protein product is called a **gene**. The expression of genes is **protein synthesis**, a process including the two steps of transcription and translation. Please see also Figure 6.5 on the next page.

The gene is a linear sequence of nucleotide bases in DNA used to establish the order of nucleotides in messenger ribonucleic acid (**mRNA**), a single-stranded nucleic acid. Being made of nucleotides, RNA molecules contain sugar, phosphate groups, and bases just like DNA. However, RNA nucleotides contain the sugar ribose instead of deoxyribose. In addition, the base uracil (U) is substituted for thymine. Each mRNA strand made by using the DNA code of a gene is called a **transcript**, and the process to make it is called **transcription**. The transcript passes through the nuclear membrane moving to a structure in the cytoplasm called a **ribosome**. The ribosome is the site of protein synthesis. The ribosome is made of rRNA and proteins. A third RNA, transfer RNA (tRNA), is required to complete protein synthesis. There are different tRNA molecules for each **amino acid** in the cytoplasm because a tRNA will pick up only one type of amino acid. Amino acids are the building blocks of **proteins**. tRNAs also have nucleotide bases; if the bases of the tRNA exactly complement the mRNA nucleotide bases, the tRNA and mRNA will bond.

How the correct proteins are built is determined by the exact base sequence of the original DNA molecule. In the gene, each grouping of three bases of DNA make a triplet **code** that is used to prepare the correct series of mRNA **codons** in the transcript. The specific mRNA codon, in turn, matches up with a particular tRNA **anticodon**. The anticodon is the series of three bases found on the tRNA molecule. Remember that the other side of each tRNA carries an amino acid. Twenty amino acids are commonly used to make proteins. Enzymes help the amino acids that are brought to the ribosome bind together to form peptides. Long chains of peptides are proteins. This step in the process of protein formation completed at the ribosome is called **translation**.

All life on Earth uses the same DNA codes to select particular amino acids! It is just by arrangement of the DNA base pairs that different mRNA codons are made, and from them, different amino acids brought by tRNA molecules to the ribosomes to make proteins. Different proteins will result in different-looking structures and enzymes. Hopefully now you understand why the production of proteins is also referred to as **gene expression**. In this activity, you will simulate the process of protein synthesis, including transcription and translation.

## Figure 6.5 Protein Synthesis

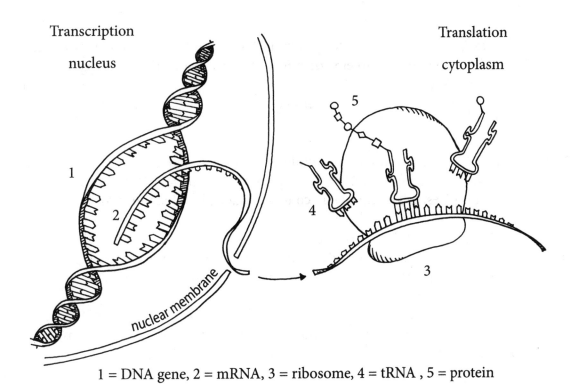

Transcription

nucleus

Translation

cytoplasm

1 = DNA gene, 2 = mRNA, 3 = ribosome, 4 = tRNA , 5 = protein

## Materials
on your lab bench
bag containing the following:
a simulated DNA gene sequence written on the outside,
white plastic cards representing mRNA codons,
blue plastic cards representing tRNA molecules with anticodons and
amino acids.

## Procedure
STEP 1. Open the bag with your DNA "gene" and materials for transcription and translation found on your lab bench.

22.  Where in the cell is the gene found?

STEP 2. Write down the DNA bases with the triplet codes you received on your bag below, and then write out the complementary mRNA transcript codons. Remember that RNA uses the base uracil instead of thymine! Select uracil to complement adenine when building mRNA.

23.   DNA triplet codes: CCT | CTT | TAC | ACA | CGG | AGG

*(handwritten below each: GGA GAA AUG UGU GCC UCC)*

mRNA codons:

STEP 3. Pull the mRNA codons you identified from your deck of rectangular mRNA cards and place them on your table in the sequence matching the DNA code sequence you determined for question 23. This is your mRNA transcript.

24.   Where in the cell does transcription occur?

*transcription occurs in the nucleus*

STEP 4. Remove the second deck of blue cards representing tRNA molecules, carrying amino acids. Find the tRNA molecules with the anticodons that complement the mRNA codons of your transcript. The anticodons are in all capital letters at the bottom of the card.

25.   What is the anticodon for AUG?

*anti codon is UAC*

STEP 5. At the top of each tRNA card is the one-letter amino acid abbreviation for the amino acid carried by that particular tRNA. We designed this exercise so that your gene can be translated into the name of an animal. The genetic code is provided in Table 6.2 on page 142.

26.   What animal did your "gene" code for?

27.   Where does translation occur in the cell?

*On a ribosome in the cytoplasm*

28. Why are there codes for "start" and "stop"?

STEP 6. Find the tRNA cards with the anticodons UCA and AGU.

29. What amino acid do these two tRNA molecules carry?

*They both code for serine*

30. Why are there two different tRNA molecules that carry the same amino acid?

*there has to be duplication w/in the system.*

31. You used just one DNA code to identify all the amino acids in your protein product. If all species on Earth use the same DNA code, then why do they look different?

*The sequence is different*

STEP 7. Put all your plastic cards back in their original bags.

## Table 6.2 The genetic code

| First base of mRNA codon | Second base of mRNA codon | | | | | | | | Third base of mRNA codon |
|---|---|---|---|---|---|---|---|---|---|
| | U | | C | | A | | G | | |
| U | UUU | Phe (F) | UCU | Ser (S) | UAU | Tyr (Y) | UGU | Cys (C) | U |
| | UUC | | UCC | | UAC | | UGC | | C |
| | UUA | Leu (L) | UCA | | UAA | Stop | UGA | Stop | A |
| | UUG | | UCG | | UAG | Stop | UGG | Trp (W) | G |
| C | CUU | Leu (L) | CCU | Pro (P) | CAU | His (H) | CGU | Arg (R) | U |
| | CUC | | CCC | | CAC | | CGC | | C |
| | CUA | | CCA | | CAA | Gln (Q) | CGA | | A |
| | CUG | | CCG | | CAG | | CGG | | G |
| A | AUU | Ile (I) | ACU | Thr (T) | AAU | Asn (N) | AGU | Ser (S) | U |
| | AUC | | ACC | | AAC | | AGC | | C |
| | AUA | | ACA | | AAA | Lys (K) | AGA | Arg (R) | A |
| | AUG | Met (M) Start | ACG | | AAG | | AGG | | G |
| G | GUU | Val (V) | GCU | Ala (A) | GAU | Asp (D) | GGU | Gly (G) | U |
| | GUC | | GCC | | GAC | | GGC | | C |
| | GUA | | GCA | | GAA | Glu (E) | GGA | | A |
| | GUG | | GCG | | GAG | | GGG | | G |

F = phenylalanine
L = leucine
I = isoleucine
M = methionine
V = valine
S = serine
P = proline
T = threonine
A = alanine
Y = tyrosine

H = histidine
Q = glutamine
N = asparagine
K = lysine
D = aspartic acid
E = glutamic acid
C = cysteine
W = tryptophan
R = arginine
G = glycine

**SUMMARY QUESTIONS**

A. Summarize from your observations what is happening in each phase of the cell cycle with respect to the movement of chromatin and chromosomes. One member of your group may be asked to share this with the class during discussion.

B. Briefly summarize the process of protein synthesis, from transcription through translation. One member of your group may be asked to share this with the class during discussion.

**POST-LAB QUESTIONS**                    **Name** _____

1.  When are cellular components replicated during the cell cycle?

2.  Why do the chromosomes look like "V"s during anaphase?

3.  Why can you not see DNA chromosomes during interphase?

4.  How is RNA different from DNA?

5.  Fully describe what happens on a ribosome.

*Questions continue on the next page.*

6. Mutations occur randomly as the result of radiation, chemical toxicity, or errors in replication. How would a mutation in the DNA sequence alter the mRNA and amino acid sequences of this gene? Underline the section of DNA that differs between the original and mutation listed below. Write out both the mRNA and amino sequence (using the genetic code).

Original DNA:           TAC-ACA-GTA-CTT-CTT-TGA-CGA-GTA-ACT
  mRNA:
 amino acids:

Mutant DNA:          TAC-ACA-GTA-TAT-ACA-TTT-CTT-TTA--ACT
  mRNA:
 amino acids:

7. When in the cell cycle does protein synthesis take place?

# MEIOSIS AND INHERITANCE

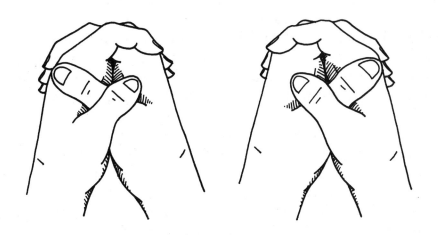

How does cell replication change when organisms reproduce sexually? Are there inheritance patterns of traits? Is there a way to predict what the offspring will look like? These questions will form the framework for your activities in today's lab.

How does cell replication change when organisms reproduce sexually? Tracking of chromosomes during cell division becomes essential in sexual reproduction. The **ploidy** of a cell indicates the number of sets of chromosomes; a **diploid** cell contains two sets. One set of chromosomes was inherited from each parent: a **maternal** set and a **paternal** set. Each set includes a complete working blueprint, that is, a copy of all the genes necessary for that individual to thrive. **Meiosis** is the special division of particular cells in jeukaryotes to reduce the total chromosome number by half for sexual reproduction. The cells produced as a result of meiosis are called **gametes**. Human gametes include spermatocytes, or sperm, produced only in the testes, and oocytes, or eggs, produced only in the ovaries. Human gametes are **haploid**, which means they only have one set of chromosomes. The reduction in chromosome sets from two to one is necessary so that the **zygote** made when the two gametes fuse, will have the same number of chromosomes as its parents. Sexual reproduction increases the **genetic variability** of the species because the offspring receive chromosomes from two parents.

As with cells that undergo mitosis, cells that undergo meiosis replicate the entire DNA during interphase. The names of the phases of meiosis follow the naming of the phases of mitosis: prophase, metaphase, anaphase, and telophase. However, there are two cell divisions in meiosis. To distinguish between these two cell divisions, the phases of meiosis are given a Roman numeral I or II. Meiosis I consists of prophase I, metaphase I, etc., while meiosis II consists of prophase II, metaphase II, etc. Between meiosis I and meiosis II there is a resting phase called **interkinesis**. You will explore other distinctions in the process of meiosis in today's lab.

Are there inheritance patterns of traits? Ranchers, who have been breeding animals for centuries in an effort to improve their stock, realize there are patterns to inheritance. A **genetic cross** results in offspring from two parents. To complete a hypothetical genetic cross, the first thing to do is identify the genes of each parent. Alternate forms of a gene are called **alleles** that result in different gene products. The gene product results in a **trait**. For example, alleles of cattle hide color are black, red, and white. The black hide of Angus cattle protects them from damaging UV radiation. If the alleles of each parent are known, a hypothetical genetic cross can be done to predict the alleles and subsequent traits of all potential offspring. If you know the hide color of the parents, you will be able to predict the hide color of the offspring.

**PRE-LAB QUESTIONS**                    **Name** _____

1.  How is the process of meiosis similar to mitosis?

2.  How is the purpose of meiosis different from mitosis?

3.  What is an allele?

4.  What is the importance of sexual reproduction?

STUDENT LEARNING OUTCOMES

Upon completion of this lab, you will be able to do the following:

> I. describe the phases of meiosis and relate meiosis to gene transfer, and
> II. predict the outcomes of a genetic cross

## I. MEIOSIS AND GENE TRANSFER

This activity has three components. First, you will learn to recognize and describe cells in the different phases of meiosis. Secondly, you will identify specific expressed traits and determine their underlying genotype. In the third part, you will put the first two steps together by simulating the steps of meiosis to produce a gamete. After simulation of fertilization, you will determine which traits are expressed in the offspring.

### I. A. Observing the phases of meiosis

In a parent cell, the maternal and paternal chromosomes that contain the same genes are called **homologous** chromosomes. During **prophase I** the replicated homologous chromosomes come together, or **synapse**. For example, the maternal chromosome number 3 synapses with the paternal chromosome number 3. The genes in each of the homologous chromosomes are oriented in the same direction when they synapse. The adjacent non-sister chromatids in each homologous pair sometimes exchange some portions (containing genes) of their chromosome, in a process called **crossing over**. This genetic exchange will increase the genetic variability of the species.

In **metaphase I**, the next phase of meiosis I, all of the homologous pairs of chromosomes line up along the metaphase plate, so that the maternal chromosome number 1 is next to the paternal chromosome number 1, and the maternal chromosome number 2 is next to the paternal chromosome number 2, etc. During **anaphase I** the homologous maternal and paternal chromosomes will separate. Which side of the metaphase plate each maternal or paternal chromosome aligns determines which of the pair goes into which daughter cell. Lining up on the metaphase I plate is random, and the way one homologous pair lines up is independent of what happens with the other pairs of chromosomes. This is important because when the gametes are made, there will be different assortments of the maternal and paternal chromosomes. For example, a gamete may have the maternal chromosome number 1 and the maternal chromosome number 2 but the paternal chromosome number 3. This shuffling of the homologous chromosomes also increases the potential for genetic variability in the species. In **telophase I**, two daughter cells are formed, and the number of chromosomes in each daughter cell is half of the number of chromosomes in the parent cell.

After the rest period, **interkinesis**, **meiosis II** is initiated. The phases of meiosis II result in the formation of daughter cells that still have half of the number of chromosomes found in the parent cell. The sister chromatids formed during interphase are separated during **anaphase II**. The cumulative result of meiosis I and meiosis II is the production of four haploid gametes from one diploid parent cell.

## Materials

on side counter
chart depicting the phases of meiosis
models of the different phases of meiosis

## Procedure

Observe the models and charts of meiosis, paying particular attention to the chromosomes. Sister chromatids still linked together at the centromere are counted as one chromosome. Answer the following questions.

1. What happens to the DNA in interphase in a cell that is going to undergo meiosis?

   Dna synthesis in interphase

2. What do the paired homologous chromosomes look like in prophase I?

   Chromosomes look like "X's.

3. If the first, or parent cell, had 16 chromosomes, how many chromosomes are in a cell at the end of metaphase I?

   16 - they havent split yet

4. If the first, or parent cell, had 16 chromosomes, how many chromosomes are in a cell at the end of anaphase I?

   the beginning of anaphase 16

5. If the first, or parent cell, had 16 chromosomes, how many chromosomes are in a cell at the end of telophase I?

   8.

### I. B. Linking alleles, genes, and traits

The alternate forms of a gene are called **alleles.** For example, the protein structure in human hair may result in smooth round shafts, making it straight. Alternatively, human hair protein structure may make the shaft flatter with bends, making hair curly. There is an allele for straight hair, and a different one for curly hair. Both are viable versions found in the species. In many cases, one of the alleles guides the production of a protein that has a distinctive look. These gene products are called **traits.** The other alleles of the gene may be hidden, or masked, because of the first gene product. Alleles that create traits that are seen are called **dominant** alleles. Alleles that create traits that can be masked by another allele are called **recessive** alleles.

By convention and for ease of discussion, the dominant allele is represented by a capital letter, and the recessive allele by the lowercase form of that letter. The two inherited genes, represented by two letters, are part of an individual's **genotype**. An individual's physical appearance is their **phenotype**.

Since humans inherit chromosomes from two parents, each person has the potential to carry two different alleles for each gene. If the two alleles of a gene are different, the individual is **heterozygous** for that gene and resulting trait. The two alleles for a gene may also be the same. If the two alleles are the same, the individual is **homozygous** for that resulting trait. A person could be homozygous dominant or homozygous recessive for a trait. However, the dominant allele is the only one seen in an individual that is heterozygous for a trait. For example, the phenotype of someone with a hairline genotype WW or Ww is "widow's peak."

You will simulate the process of meiosis to produce a gamete, and trace the movement of alleles from nine genes from the parent to the child.

### Materials
>       on side counter
>               PTC paper

### Procedure
STEP 1. Complete Table 7.1 on the next page by determining your phenotype and genotype for the traits listed. These traits follow conventional dominance patterns.

## Table 7.1 Individual phenotypes and genotypes

| trait | dominant allele | recessive allele | your phenotype | your genotype |
|---|---|---|---|---|
| hairline | W = widow's peak | w = straight hairline | WW | |
| PTC tasting | T = present | t = absent | T | |
| bent little finger | B = bent | b = straight | | |
| earlobes | A = free | a = attached | A | |
| thumb position when interlacing fingers | C = left over right | c = right over left | C | |
| mid-digital hair | M = present | m = absent | m m | |
| tongue-rolling | R = present | r = absent | R | |
| freckles on the face | Q = present | q = absent | qq | |
| cleft in chin | L = present | l = absent | ll | |

6. Are you able to enter your compete genotype if you have a dominant phenotype?

no

STEP 2. Select a recessive phenotype observed in your lab group, and formulate a hypothesis regarding the frequency of that recessive trait in the classroom.

7. Hypothesis:

STEP 3. To test your hypothesis, gather and input the class data on the frequency of each phenotype in Table 7.2 on the next page.

Dominant: B
first letter in dominant
trait. capital - need only
one copy of gene

Recessive : need copy of gene
from mom and dad - 2 copies
little case - bb

Phenotype: physical appearance of trait

Genotype: genetic make up

Brown hair

B

Red hair

bb

Brown hair

Bb

**Table 7.2 Classroom phenotype frequencies**

| trait | dominant phenotype | number in class | recessive phenotype | number in class |
|---|---|---|---|---|
| hairline | W = widow's peak | 11 | w = straight hairline | 10 |
| PTC tasting | T = present | 16 | t = absent | 5 |
| bent little finger | B = bent | | b = straight | |
| earlobes | A = free | 15 | a = attached | 6 |
| thumb position when interlacing fingers | C = left over right | 12 | c = right over left | 9 |
| mid-digital hair | M = present | 5 | m = absent | 16 |
| tongue-rolling | R = present | 15 | r = absent | 6 |
| freckles on the face | Q = present | 2 | q = absent | 19 |
| cleft in chin | L = present | 5 | l = absent | 14 |

STEP 4. Analyze the data you collected to test your hypothesis.

    8.  Do the data support or refute your hypothesis?

## I. C. Gametogenesis and inheritance

Each person has one allele for each trait that they received from their mother and one from their father. **Maternal chromosomes** contain alleles passed from the mother. The **paternal chromosomes** contain alleles that originated from the father.

In this exercise, you will simulate the process of producing a gamete (gametogenesis), and then use one of the gametes to make a hypothetical child. You will build your homologous chromosomes, replicate them, and then produce a gamete that contains your selected traits. You will simulate fertilization with another gamete that was made by another lab group. To conclude, you will determine the phenotype and genotype of your child. Colored beads will be used to represent genes. Solid colored beads represent the dominant allele and striped beads of the same color represent the recessive allele for that gene.

### Materials
    on side counter
        cups with solid and striped colored beads
        cup with yellow links representing centromeres
        cup with red links representing centromeres

    on your lab bench
        resealable bag with gender identified
        dice
        sets of 8 papers with large circles

### Procedure
STEP 1. Take your resealable bag to the side counter and add four beads of each solid color and striped color to the bag. Also pick up two red centromere links and two yellow centromere links from the side counter to use in your simulation of meiotic divisions.

STEP 2. Return to your desk and randomly pull a bead from the bag. That bead represents the first of the maternal alleles. Set that bead aside to use later in building the maternal chromosome.

STEP 3. Continue selecting beads randomly to generate an **adult genotype**. The first bead of a color will represent the maternal allele, and the second bead of the same color will represent the paternal allele. Set the beads you select aside to use later in building your chromosomes. Record your selections in Table 7.3 below. (Refer back to Table 7.1 for the genotype letters associated with each phenotype.)

### Table 7.3 Adult phenotype and genotype

| trait | geno-type letter | bead color | maternal alleles | paternal alleles | adult genotype | adult phenotype |
|---|---|---|---|---|---|---|
| hairline | w | purple | | | | |
| PTC tasting | t | white | | | | |
| bent little finger | b | orange | | | | |
| earlobes | a | yellow | | | | |
| thumb position when interlac-ing fingers | c | blue | | | | |
| mid-digital hair | m | green | | | | |
| tongue-rolling | r | red | | | | |
| freckles on the face | q | pink | | | | |
| cleft in chin | l | black | | | | |

STEP 4. Complete the drawing of your adult by adding the phenotypes of the traits you selected on Figure 7.1 below. Circle the correct thumb position. Check mark if PTC tasting is present or absent. Check mark if a bent little finger is present or absent.

**Figure 7.1 Adult phenotype**

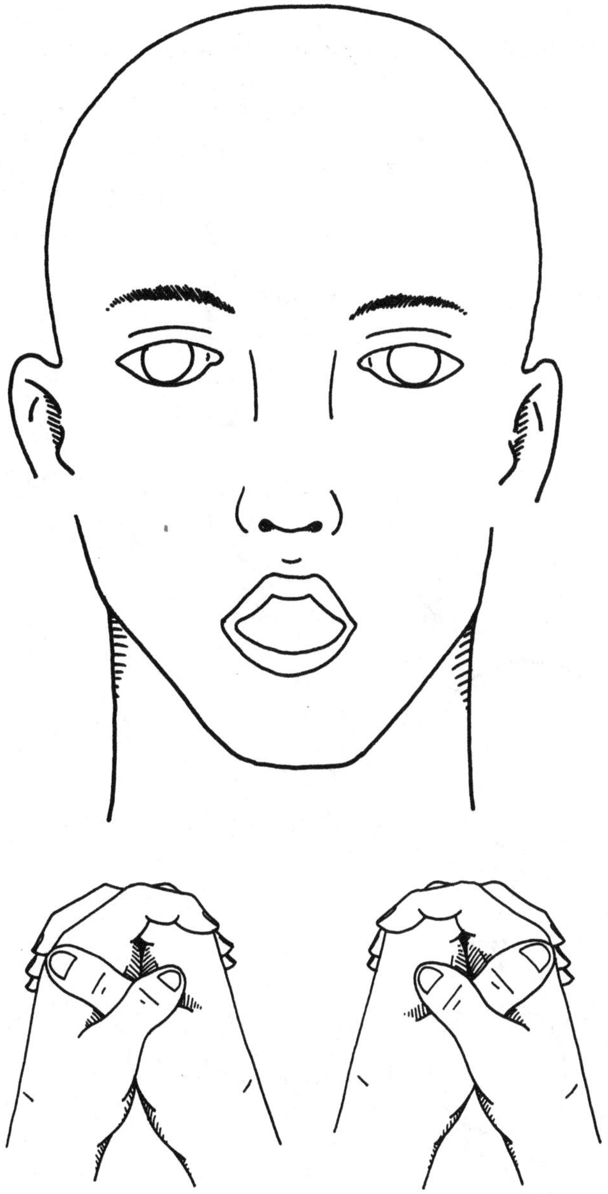

PTC tasting            present _____ absent _____

bent little finger     present _____ absent _____

STEP 5. Set up the eight paper circles on your lab bench to match Figure 7.2 below.

**Figure 7.2 The steps of meiosis**

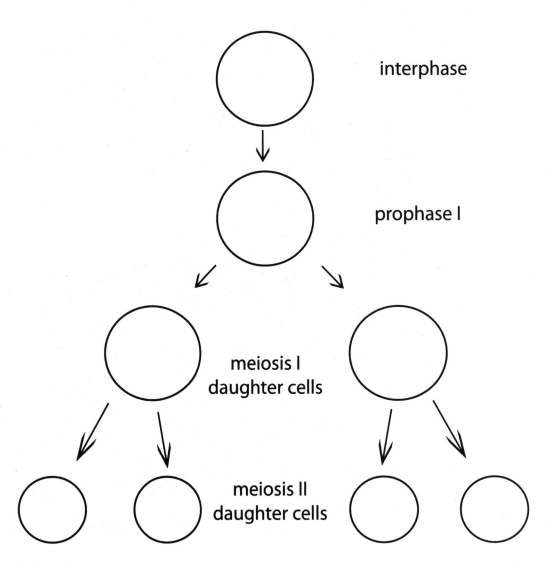

interphase

prophase I

meiosis I
daughter cells

meiosis II
daughter cells

STEP 6. Genes are located in particular order at specific places, or **loci** (singular: locus), on a chromosome. Build your maternal and paternal chromosomes with the order of traits *exactly* as listed on Table 7.3 with the solid and striped beads you selected. *The centromeres will be placed between the green and red beads.* Beads above the centromere will be connected with the nub facing downward, and those below should have the nubs facing upward towards the centromere. Use a red centromere for the maternal chromosome, and a yellow centromere for the paternal chromosome.

The pair of homologous chromosomes you built will now be used to learn the process of meiosis. The first step is chromosome replication during interphase.

STEP 7. Replicate each chromosome by using additional beads from your bag, and place them on the interphase circle on your lab bench. The sister chromatids remain attached at the end of interphase, looking like an "X".

9. How many replicated chromosomes does your parent cell have at the end of interphase?

10. How many genes for traits do you have on each chromosome?

STEP 8. Move your chromosomes to the prophase I circle. Simulate the process of the formation of a synapse. To simulate crossing over, you will exchange the last three genes between the non-sister chromatids of the homologous pair. That is, the red, pink, and black beads will be swapped from a maternal chromatid with those on a paternal chromatid.

11. Why is it important that the two homologous chromosomes are oriented in the same direction?

STEP 9. Separate the paternal and maternal chromosomes into the circles representing the meiosis I daughter cells.

12. How many chromosomes are in each meiosis I daughter cell?

13.  Are the meiosis I daughter cells haploid or diploid?

STEP 10. Separate the sister chromatids of each chromosome into the circles representing meiosis I daughter cells, and place one in each of the meiosis II daughter cells.

14.  What is the name of the meiotic phase that separates the sister chromatids?

15.  Are all the gametes produced the same? Explain why or why not.

STEP 11. On Figure 7.2 shown previously in your manual, draw out the process of meiosis with lines to represent your chromosomes. You may use colored pencils, or straight, dashed, or "wiggle" lines to distinguish between the maternal and paternal chromosomes.

Meiosis II daughter cells are potential gametes.

16.  How many chromosomes are in each meiosis II daughter cell?

17.  Are the gametes haploid or diploid?

Human gametes produced in the testes in men are called spermatocytes that develop into sperm, and gametes produced in the ovaries of women are called oocytes that develop into eggs.

18.  Check the gender on the resealable bag on your lab bench. Which type of gamete did your hypothetical adult produce?

STEP 12. Simulate the process of random selection of gametes. Number your gametes one through four and roll a die to determine which gamete will be selected for fertilization. If you roll a five or six, roll again.

STEP 13. Simulate the process of fertilization by taking your gamete and matching is up with that of another lab group. If you have an egg, find a lab group that produced sperm.

STEP 14. Roll the die to select one of their sperm. Note that it may be a different gamete than that table selected for mating with your egg!

STEP 15. Write out the genotype and phenotype of your offspring for each of the nine traits in Table 7.4 on the next page.

**Table 7.4 Offspring genotypes and phenotypes**

| trait | geno-type letter | bead color | maternal allele (contributed by egg) | paternal allele (contributed by sperm) | offspring phenotype |
|---|---|---|---|---|---|
| hairline | w | purple | | | |
| PTC tasting | t | white | | | |
| bent little finger | b | orange | | | |
| earlobes | a | yellow | | | |
| thumb position when interlacing fingers | c | blue | | | |
| mid-digital hair | m | green | | | |
| tongue-rolling | r | red | | | |
| freckles on the face | q | pink | | | |
| cleft in chin | l | black | | | |

STEP 16. DRAW the phenotypic traits of your child on Figure 7.3 below based on the results recorded in Table 7.4. Circle the correct thumb position. Check mark if PTC tasting is present or absent. Check mark if a bent little finger is present or absent.

**Figure 7.3 Child phenotype**

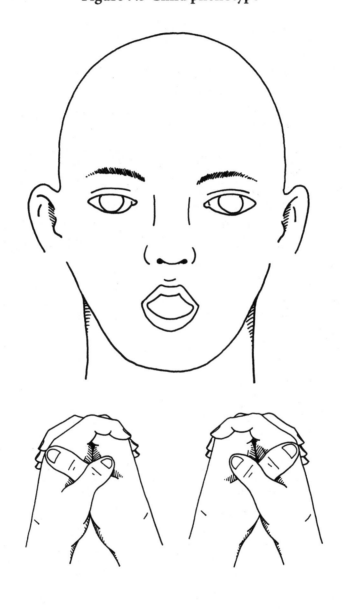

PTC tasting                 present _____ absent _____

bent little finger          present _____ absent _____

19. Compare your baby to the drawings of each parent. Does your baby look exactly like you or the other parent? Explain your answer.

STEP 17. Return all the materials for this exercise, including beads and centromere links to their respective cups and containers.

## II. INHERITANCE AND PREDICTIONS

This activity has four parts. First, you will learn how to use Punnett squares, to predict the outcomes of a genetic cross. In the other three parts, you will use Punnett squares to make predictions of the outcomes of (1) a monohybrid cross with traditional dominance patterns, (2) a cross where alleles are co-dominant, and (3) a cross where alleles share expression, or are incompletely dominant. You will test your predictions of the monohybrid cross and the co-dominant cross.

### II. A. Using Punnett squares

A **Punnett square** is used to visualize the different possible combinations of alleles when two individuals mate. This tool used to predict the ratio of possible outcomes of a genetic cross.

20. If a parent is heterozygous for earlobe attachment, what is their phenotype?

You can set up a Punnett square to determine if all offspring of two parents who are both heterozygous for earlobe attachment will look like their parents for that trait. The alleles contributed by each parent are placed on each side of the square. The interior of the square is filled in with the intersection of the alleles as shown in Figure 7.4 on the next page.

**Figure 7.4 A Punnett square**

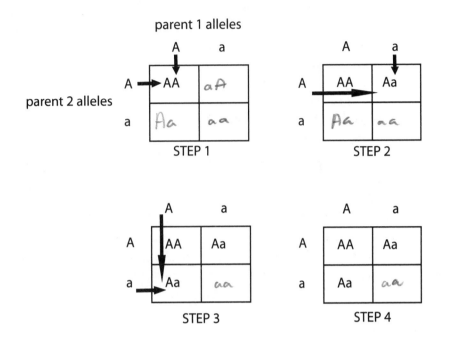

**Procedure**

Complete Step 4 of Figure 7.4 by filling in the empty square.

21. Will all the potential offspring of the parents in the example above have earlobe attachment the same as their parents? Explain.

To be able to use a Punnett square, you need to know the genotype of each parent. If given a written problem, translate the description of the trait of each parent into the two-letter genotype for that trait. For example, a parent who is heterozygous for earlobe attachment has the genotype Aa.

22. What is the genotype for an individual who has straight little fingers?

## II. B. The monohybrid cross

A cross between two heterozygous parents is called a **monohybrid cross**. The "mono" indicated that only one trait is under consideration, and the "hybrid" means that there are two different alleles. A hybrid individual is heterozygous for a trait. In this exercise, you will explore actual outcomes versus predicted offspring ratios of a monohybrid cross. Individual corn kernels on an ear of corn contain the embryo resulting from fertilization of a corn egg. Corn kernels may be purple or yellow. Purple kernels (P) are dominant over yellow (r).

### Materials

on your lab bench

corn cob from a monohybrid cross of purple and yellow kernels
pipe cleaner

### Procedure

STEP 1. Predict the expected outcomes of purple kernels to yellow kernels in an ear of corn from a monohybrid cross by completing the Punnett square of Figure 7.5 below to see all expected offspring genotypes.

**Figure 7.5 Punnett square of a monohybrid cross**

P = Purple        PP        parent 1 alleles

p : Yellow        Pp
                  PP

parent 2 alleles

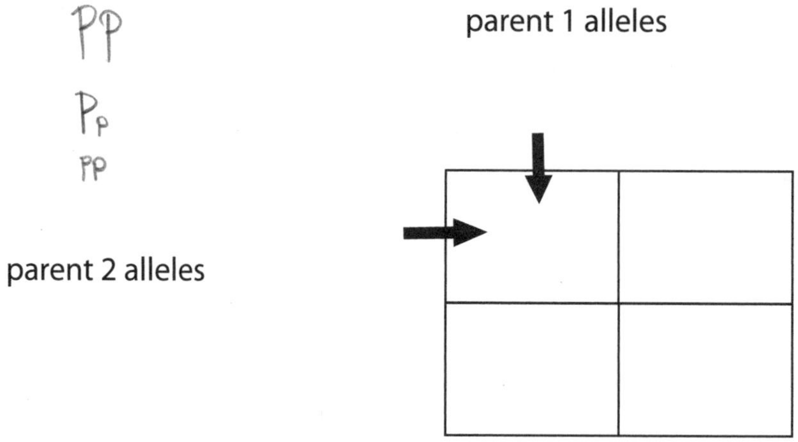

STEP 2. Now write the *phenotype* (purple or yellow) under the genotype in each square of Figure 7.5.

Each square represents 25% of the total possible offspring. If two squares result in the same outcome, then the expected percentage of offspring with that genotype or phenotype is the sum of those two squares.

23.   What is the predicted percentage of corn kernels that will be purple?

STEP 3. Locate a hybridized ear of corn on your lab bench. Use the pipe cleaner to count lengthwise the total number of kernels in five rows on the ear, and enter it below. Then count the number of purple kernels in those five rows.

24.  total number of kernels _____173_____

number of purple kernels _____128_____

STEP 4. Divide the number of purple kernels by the total number of kernels in the five rows to calculate the percentage of purple kernels in your sample.

25.  The percentage of purple/total kernels _____73.9% = 74%_____

Note: When there is a large number of offspring, as in the corn, the actual percentages come close to the predicted ratios determined by the Punnett square. However, each cross is independent and people do not have hundreds of children. It is possible that the heterozygous parents with free earlobes never have a child with attached earlobes; each child they have has a 1 in 4 chance of having attached earlobes.

## II. C. Traits that show co-dominance

Some gene products are evident in an individual as long is the allele is present. Specific surface markers may be present on the red blood cell, and their presence accounts for the standard ABO blood typing. If a person does not have the allele for that red blood cell surface marker, and it is introduced to their body, the marker is identified as an **antigen**. Antigens are foreign elements that promote an immune response. In blood, the response is the production of antibodies specific to the marker. These antibodies clump the blood and make it non-functional.

The four blood types in humans are A, B, AB, and O. A and B stand for specific antigens, and O is the absence of A and B antigens. If a person has type A blood, they have the A-antigen. Also, if a person with type A blood were to receive a transfusion of type B blood, their body would see the type B blood as foreign and have antibodies to destroy the red blood cells of the type B blood.

In this activity, you will determine the blood type of Ms. Smith, Mr. Green, Mr. Brown, and Ms. Jones. You will use the results by setting up Punnett squares to determine who might be the father of Ms. Smith's child based on their blood types.

**Materials**

on your lab bench
- depression plates
- wax pencil
- beaker for waste
- antiserum A
- antiserum B
- toothpicks
- synthetic blood samples representing
    - Smith
    - Green
    - Brown
    - Jones

**Procedure**

STEP 1. You will use a ceramic plate with depression wells to test the blood specimens. The testing order of your samples will be Smith, Green, Brown, and Jones. The well for Smith will be on the left. *Keep the plate flat on the bench throughout the experiment.*

**Figure 7.6 Depression well plate**

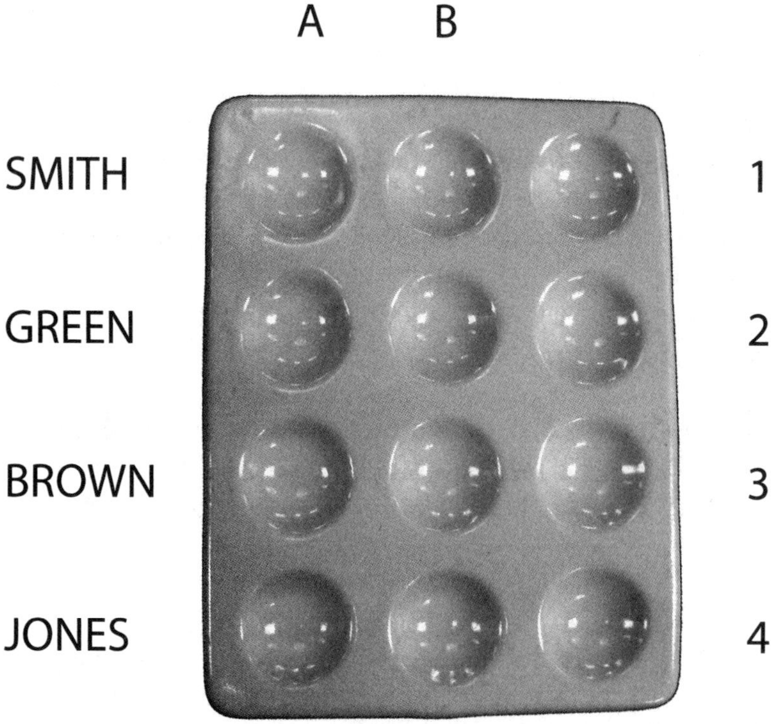

STEP 2. Use your wax pencil to mark the first column of the depression well "A", and the middle column "B." Mark the rows 1 through 4 on the right-hand side of the plate. Please refer to Figure 7.6 on the previous page.

STEP 3. Put one drop of the A antiserum in the four depressions of the first column marked "A" on the plate.

STEP 4. Put one drop of the B antiserum in each of the four depressions of the middle column marked "B" on the plate.

STEP 5. Gently agitate the synthetic blood sample of Smith, and put one drop of the synthetic blood in the "A" well and one drop of blood in the "B" well of row 1.

STEP 6. Using *clean* toothpicks *each* time, stir the blood and antiserum within each well. Dispose of the toothpicks in the waste container. Let the Smith test sit while you go onto the next step.

STEP 7. Gently agitate the synthetic blood sample of Green, and put one drop of the synthetic blood in the "A" well and one drop of blood in the "B" well of row 2. Using *clean* toothpicks *each* time, stir the blood and antiserum within each well. Dispose of the toothpicks in the waste container. Let the Green test sit while you go onto the next step.

STEP 8. Gently agitate the synthetic blood sample of Brown, and put one drop of the synthetic blood in the "A" well and one drop of blood in the "B" well of row 3. Using *clean* toothpicks *each* time, stir the blood and antiserum within each well. Dispose of the toothpicks in the waste container. Let the Brown test sit while you go onto the next step.

STEP 9. Gently agitate the synthetic blood sample of Jones, and put one drop of the synthetic blood in the "A" well and one drop of blood in the "B" well of row 4. Using *clean* toothpicks *each* time, stir the blood and antiserum within each well. Dispose of the toothpicks in the waste container. Let the Jones test sit while you go onto the next step.

STEP 10. Wait two minutes. If the blood sample clumped with an antiserum, that blood contains that marker. For example, clumping with the A antiserum means the blood has the A antigen. Someone with the A antigen has Type A blood. Look for clumping in each of the wells.

STEP 11. Record your results in Table 7.5 on the next page by marking a "+" for clumping and a "-" for the absence of clumping. Determine the blood type and have your instructor check your results.

**Table 7.5. Sample blood types**

| sample Name | result with A antigen | result with B antigen | Blood type |
|---|---|---|---|
| Smith | + | − | A |
| Green | + | + | AB |
| Brown | ◯ | ◯ | ◯ |
| Jones | − | + | B |

26.  Instructor initials _____.

Since every human is diploid, each person has two alleles at the gene locus for the ABO blood type markers. Since the ABO blood type markers exhibit phenotypic codominance, a letter with a superscript is used to represent the genotypes. For example, someone with Type A blood has the genotype $I^A$. Their second copy of the gene may have the allele $I^A$ or it may have i, representing no surface marker. Their genotype would be written $I^A I^A$ or $I^A i$. Similarly, someone with Type B blood could have either $I^B I^B$ or $I^B i$ genotypes.

27.  How do you represent the genotype of a person with Type AB blood?

AB

STEP 12. Complete the possible genotypes in Table 7.6 on the next page, based on the results recorded in Table 7.5.

**Table 7.6. Sample genotypes**

| sample name | blood type | possible genotypes |
|---|---|---|
| Smith | A | AO, AA |
| Green | AB | AB |
| Brown | O | Oo |
| Jones | B | BO |

28.  Suppose Smith is the mother of Jones. What is Ms. Smith's genotype? Explain why.

STEP 13. Complete the Punnett squares below, evaluating whether Green or Brown could be the father of Jones.

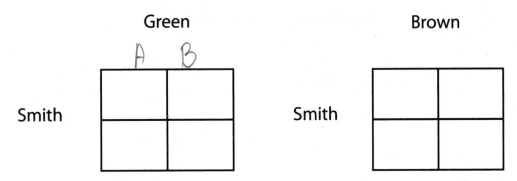

29.  Based on the blood sample data, which of the men could be the father of Ms. Jones? Explain your answer.

STEP 14. Clean and dry the depression plates.

## II. D. Traits that are incompletely dominant

Paper

As you saw in the last activity, both copies of some alleles are represented in the phenotype, so are considered co-dominant. Other traits have alleles that share in the final look, so are considered incompletely dominant. In cases of incomplete dominance, genotype letters for both forms of the allele are provided in superscript format. For example, snapdragon flower color may be red ($C^rC^r$), white ($C^wC^w$), or pink ($C^rC^w$). The pink color indicates that both the red and white alleles are present.

**Materials**

on side counter

chart of pink, white, and red snapdragons
charts demonstrating different genetic crosses

**Procedure**

Complete the Punnett square showing the cross between a red snapdragon and a pink snapdragon.

red snapdragon

pink snapdragon

| | |
|---|---|
| | |
| | |

30.  What proportion of the offspring will be pink?

**SUMMARY QUESTIONS**

A. In one or two paragraphs, explain the process of meiosis and relate it to the transfer of traits from one generation to another. One member of your group may be asked to share this with the class during discussion.

B. Summarize in your own words how Punnett squares can be used to make predictions about the traits in offspring. One member of your group may be asked to share this with the class during discussion.

blood types - A B AB O—no receptors

RH+- receptors

RH- — no receptor

codominate: both are expressed
genotype- genetic make up

| Phenotype | Genotype | |
|-----------|----------|---|
| A | AA, AO | A or O blood |
| B | BB, BO | B or o blood |
| AB | AB | universal recipient |
| O | OO | universal donor only receive "O" blood |

**POST-LAB QUESTIONS**                     Name _____

1. How does meiosis increase the genetic variability of a species?

2. Can a man pass on traits located on his maternal chromosomes? Explain your answer.

3. What is the difference between a person's genotype and their phenotype?

4. If the trait of an allele is "dominant", does that mean it is more frequently seen in the population? Explain your answer.

5. Two parents who are both heterozygous for a trait have four children. The first three show the dominant phenotype. Does their fourth child have the recessive phenotype? Explain your answer.

6. Explain the difference between co-dominant and incompletely dominant traits.

*Questions continue on the next page.*

7. A "test cross" is particular type of genetic cross with a parent that has the phenotype of the dominant allele, but their genotype is unknown. Mating the parent with the unknown genotype with an individual of the recessive phenotype makes the test cross. For example, brown (B) hair coat is dominant over yellow (b) in Labrador retrievers. If you cross a brown lab with a yellow lab you will be able to determine the genotype for hair color of the brown lab parent by looking at the offspring. Explain how this works.

# VARIABILITY WITHIN A SPECIES AND NATURAL SELECTION

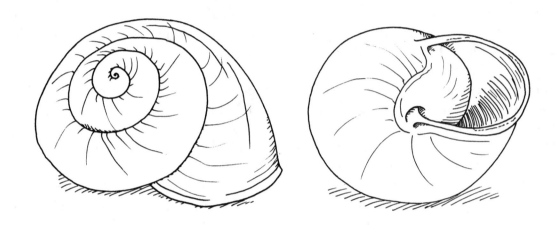

What is a species? What is a population? How do differences among individuals in a population affect the survival of the species? How does natural selection bring about change? These questions will form the framework for your activities in today's lab.

The term **species** means "kind" or "type". The biological definition of a species counts organisms that can breed together and produce viable and fertile offspring. All the members of a species that live in one location represent a **population** of that species. Populations differ in the amount of variation there is among members of the population. Variations among the members of a population are the result of the accumulation of random mutations in the genes. The term **gene pool** is used to refer to the sum of all the genes of all the individuals in a population. A population of a species therefore consists of freely interbreeding individuals that share a common gene pool. **Gene flow** between populations occurs with migrations of individuals to and from one population to other populations of the species, so immigration and emigration also affect the quality and extent of the gene pool. As you would expect, gene flow reduces the differences between populations.

How do differences among individuals in a population affect the survival of the entire species? The look, behavior, and physiology of individuals vary within a population due to fundamental genetic differences. The end result of these individual differences is intrapopulation **variability** of phenotypes. Each individual will have a different ability to survive and reproduce when challenged with changing conditions of their environment. For example, those that can swim better will be more likely to survive a flood. The environmental challenges may be biological as well. For example, an increase in the number of wolves will threaten the survival of rabbits. Those that survive a physical or biological challenge, and are able to have offspring, contribute disproportionately more of their genes to the gene pool of the next generation than those individuals who fail to thrive and reproduce. Those individuals with unfavorable traits for an environmental challenge will not reproduce and/or die. This collectively is the process of **natural selection**.

How does natural selection bring about change in a population? Because the environment is always changing, there are always both physical and biological challenges. More examples include a cold winter or drought may limit plant growth, habitable land may be washed away in a storm, or there may be an increase in competing species. If there exists an adequate diversity of individual phenotypes within a population, it is more likely that at least some members of the population will survive these challenges and be naturally selected. Because their genotype determines their phenotype, it is their genes that will remain in the gene pool. The extent of genetic variability in populations of a species is therefore very important to biologists. Naturally selecting the most fit individual is fundamental to population variability. Due to gene pool changes from generation to generation due to natural selection, the population changes. The term for change is **evolution**. Fit individuals are naturally selected, but the unit of change for that species is the population itself. Because of inter-population variability, one population of a species may evolve with naturally selected genes that enable it to survive when other populations of that species may dwindle in number or disappear.

**PRE-LAB QUESTIONS**                                    Name _____

1.  What is the difference between a species and a population?

    A species means a kind or type, that can breed together and produce viable and fertile offspring. A population is all the members of a species that live in one location

2.  Why do we see so much variation among individual members of animal and plant populations?

    due accumulation of random mutations in the genes

3.  What is meant by the term "gene pool?"

    gene pool is the sum of all genes of all the individuals in a population.

4.  What is natural selection?

    Physical and biological changes in a population

## STUDENT LEARNING OUTCOMES

Upon completion of today's lab, you will be able to do the following:

I. describe population variability, and

II. explain the impact of genetic variability on natural selection

## I. VARIABILITY WITHIN A SPECIES

In this activity, you will identify individual phenotypical differences in a sample of shells from a terrestrial snail population as a basis to measure population variation. You will identify three traits in your sample specimens to evaluate the amount and the nature of variation in your sample. Later, you will trade your sample with two other groups so that you can compare the smaller sample variability with the variability found in the larger population. You will use these data to describe the distribution of these characters in the snail population through statistical calculation and graphs.

The shells you are examining were synthesized slowly by the mollusks that lived inside at one time.

1. What is an advantage of having a shell?

Protection

## Materials

on your lab bench

tray of snail shells

ruler

calipers

string

scale

## Procedure

STEP 1. Compare your shells to Figure 8.1 on the next page to learn the names of key structures.

**Figure 8.1 Structures of a snail shell**

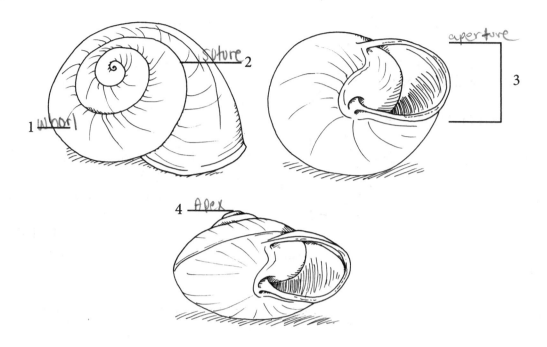

**(1) whorl**: a circular turn around the apex
**(2) suture**: line between successive whorls
**(3) aperture**: orifice of the last complete turn allowing the head and foot of the mollusk to exit; it also withdraws into its shell through this opening
**(4) apex**: crown from which the shell grows

2. List at least five ways in which your sample shells exhibit *intrapopulation variation*.

 - Color
 - size
 - whorl
 - weight
 - rigidness

STEP 2. Select three physical traits to investigate further.

3. Put the traits you selected on the drawing in Figure 8.2 on the next page to show exactly what you have chosen to measure.

size
weight of shell

**Figure 8.2 Structures selected to study**

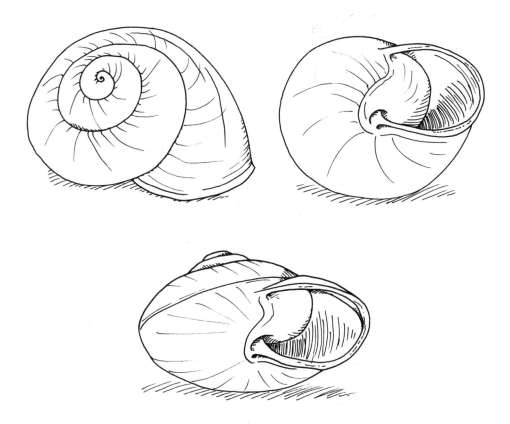

STEP 3. Measure the selected three traits in your 15-specimen sample and record your data in Table 8.1 on the next page. Record the specimen box number, the trait and unit of measure in the top row.

**Table 8.1 Selected trait distribution in sample of snails**

| specimen box no. *table 5* | trait A: *aperture size* unit: mm | trait B: *weight* unit: g | trait C: *# of whorl* unit: |
|---|---|---|---|
| shell 1 | 35 | 45.79 | 5 |
| shell 2 | 36 | 38.81 | 5 |
| shell 3 | 35 | 42.93 | 5 |
| shell 4 | 38 | 53.18 | 5 |
| shell 5 | 40 | 34.39 | 5 |
| shell 6 | 33 | 41.36 | 5 |
| shell 7 | 34 | 39.49 | 5 |
| shell 8 | 35 | 32.59 | 5 |
| shell 9 | 33 | 45.98 | 5 |
| shell 10 | 34 | 43.67 | 5 |
| shell 11 | 35 | 37.83 | 5 |
| shell 12 | 36 | 52.35 | 5 |
| shell 13 | 32 | 44.88 | 5 |
| shell 14 | 40 | 40.45 | 5 |
| shell 15 | 37 | 32.28 | 5 |

STEP 4. Identify the smallest and largest values to calculate the **range**. The range is calculated by subtracting the smallest value from the largest value.

4. trait A:  smallest 32mm , largest 40mm, range 8m

trait B:  smallest 32.28 , largest 53.18 , range 20.9

trait C:  smallest 5 , largest 5 , range 0

5.  Which of your three traits shows the greatest range?

weight

STEP 5. The trait with the greatest range has the greatest variability. Measure 30 more specimens by trading your specimen tray with other groups so that you can measure the trait you determined had the greatest variability in at least 45 shells, representing a population. Record your data in Table 8.2 below. Record the specimen box numbers to make sure you do not repeat samples.

**Table 8.2. Selected trait distribution in a population of snails**

| specimen box no. | trait: | specimen box no. | trait: |
|---|---|---|---|
| 4 | unit: weight | 6 | unit: weight |
| shell 16 | 47.43 | shell 31 | 32.38 |
| shell 17 | 32.26 | shell 32 | 56.47 |
| shell 18 | 39.74 | shell 33 | 39.49 |
| shell 19 | 40.71 | shell 34 | 42.43 |
| shell 20 | 34.62 | shell 35 | 42.07 |
| shell 21 | 38.77 | shell 36 | 41.07 |
| shell 22 | 28.44 | shell 37 | 39.12 |
| shell 23 | 24.89 | shell 38 | 37.27 |
| shell 24 | 31.68 | shell 39 | 45.34 |
| shell 25 | 39.59 | shell 40 | 46.25 |
| shell 26 | 46.06 | shell 41 | 43.83 |
| shell 27 | 46.72 | shell 42 | 60.92 |
| shell 28 | 38.77 | shell 43 | 46.43 |
| shell 29 | 42.41 | shell 44 | 37.62 |
| shell 30 | 35.36 | shell 45 | 40.92 |

STEP 6. Identify the smallest and largest values to calculate the range of your selected trait in the population of 45.

6.  smallest ___2.489___, largest ___60.92___, range ___86.03___

7.  How is the range for the sample size of 15 different from the population of 45?

    larger range

8.  What happened to the size of the gene pool?

    It gets bigger

9.  Can you think of any advantage to an individual at one extreme or the other of the population with respect to this variable?

    If you're small stay hidden
    if you're large you can see more.

STEP 7. Calculate the **mean** of your selected trait for both the sample set of 15 shells, and the larger population set of 45. The mean is calculated by dividing the sum of all the values of a set by the number of values in that set. In the sample set, you have 15 values.

10.  mean of sample size 15 ___41.73___

11.  mean of population size 45 ___41.01___

12.  Does your initial sample represent the population with respect to this trait? Explain your answer.

    yes

13.  Where did the variability of this trait come from?
    yes with nature and nurture.

You will now use your data to prepare a new kind of graph. The values you have collected are examples of continuous data. **Continuous data** are measurement data that can assume any value in an interval. (This is different from discrete data that is counting data.) When graphing a single variable against frequency, it is called a **histogram**. Histograms differ from a "regular" bar graph because the x-axis will show continuous data.

STEP 8. Begin your preparation for the graph by sorting your data into a **frequency table**. To complete a frequency table, values are sorted into equally sized intervals. The total range divided by the number of intervals used determines the interval size.

$$\frac{\text{total range of data}}{\text{number of intervals}} = \text{interval size}$$

For example, if you want to sort by shell weight, and sample shell weights were between 9.6 grams and 1.2 grams, your total range is 9.6 g – 1.2 g, or 8.4 g. If you want to sort into six equal intervals, then divide the range by six; in this example 8.4 g /6. Each interval would be 8.4 g /6, or 1.4 g wide.

$$\frac{9.6\text{ g} - 1.2\text{ g (range)}}{6\text{ (number of intervals)}} = 1.4\text{ g (interval size)}$$

14. Enter the range of data values from your sample size of 45 into the equation to determine your interval size for six intervals.

$$\frac{\text{(range)}}{6} = \underline{\hspace{1.5cm}} \text{ (interval size)}$$

Continuing with our example, if each interval is 1.4 g., the first interval would be completed by adding 1.4 g. to the first value. In this example, the intervals would be: 1.2-2.6 g, 2.6-4.0 g, 4.0-5.4g, etc.

STEP 9. Write your six interval values into the first column of Table 8.3 on the next page. The start of the first interval is the smallest value you identified in question 6, on the previous page. Add the value you calculated in question 14, above, to determine the end of the first inverval. The second interval begins with the end value of the first interval.

STEP 10. The frequency of shells found in each interval is the count of how many of your shells belong in each interval. If a value is on the border of two intervals, include it in the higher interval. (Tip: Have a lab partner read off the trait values while you keep tally marks in the correct intervals, then add up the tally marks to get the count, or frequency, for each interval.) Complete Table 8.3 on the next page.

**Table 8.3. Frequency table of the number of shells found within each interval**

| interval values | tally marks | frequency (number of shell measurements within this range) |
|---|---|---|
|  |  |  |
|  |  |  |
|  |  |  |
|  |  |  |
|  |  |  |
|  |  |  |

STEP 11. Prepare a histogram using the graph paper at the end of the lab. Label the x-axis with the interval values and the y-axis with the frequency, and then draw in the bars. Try to use as much of the graph area as possible. Title your graph. Note: your bars should be touching each other. See also Appendix F, Frequency data and histograms.

## II. GENETIC VARIABILITY AND NATURAL SELECTION

In this activity, you will follow the course of natural selection from generation to generation in a population of birds. A great deal of genetic variation exists in this population. We will focus on the individual variation seen in the beak shapes of these birds. Because of the different shapes of their beaks, the individual birds in this population will use their beaks to eat in different ways.

Though these birds can eat any of the following foods to survive, some birds prefer to eat certain things. This is because individuals with particular beak shapes have an easier time obtaining and eating certain foods. Right now, conditions are good and there are many different types of food available in this environment. These birds normally eat berries, worms, insects, and seeds.

**Materials**

> on instructor's bench
>> carpet
>> watch or stopwatch
>> calculator
>> beans (types of seeds)
>> strings (to represent worms)
>> large container for holding food per class
>> one paper cup per student
>> one feeding mechanism per student:
>>> drinking straw
>>> a pair of pencils
>>> tweezers
>>> clothespin
>>> stick
>>> spoon

*(handwritten: 18 + 13 = 31)*

*(handwritten: (16)   18   44)*

**Procedure**

*(handwritten: 8 w    9 RB    8 spek    137)*

STEP 1.  Hypothesize what kinds of food each bird eats with its beak and how it uses its beak to eat its food. Record you hypotheses in Table 8.4 below.

**Table 8.4. The influence of beak shape on food eaten**

| beak shape | type of food eaten | how beak is used |
|---|---|---|
| drinking straw shaped | | |
| tweezer shaped | | |
| pencil shaped | | |
| stick shaped | | |
| clothespin shaped | | |
| spoon shaped | | |

*(handwritten right margin: 8 / 9 / 17)*

STEP 2. Disaster has struck this population of birds! Sudden changes in the climate have altered the environment so that now only a few worms and seeds are available and the entire population of birds must eat worms or seeds in order to survive. Unfortunately, the worms and seeds are in short supply. If birds having a certain beak shape fail to obtain food and therefore die, they will not be able to produce offspring. The genetic traits of the parent birds will not be passed on to the younger generations.

15.   If seeds and worms are the only available food, hypothesize which beak phenotype will be the most successful? Explain your reasoning.

*Spoons*

16.   If seeds and worms are the only available food, hypothesize which beak phenotype will be the least successful? Explain your reasoning.

*Sticks or pencils*

STEP 3. Your instructor will divide the class into groups. Each group of students represents a group of individual birds having the same beak shape (feeding mechanism). Each member of the group should get one of the feeding mechanisms (beak), and a mouth (cup).

STEP 4. You will try to get food using your "beak" during five rounds of play. You will be competing with each other to capture seeds and worms. The instructor will throw the food onto an area rug. You should face away from the hunting area while the food is being thrown out. When the instructor gives the signal, you will try to capture seeds and worms as fast as you can until *stop* is called. You will have about 15 seconds to capture food during each round. Please read and follow the following rules of the hunt.

**Rules of the hunt**
1. Food must be *lifted* with the feeding mechanism (beak) and placed into the "mouth" (cup) held in the opposite hand. You cannot shove the food in by pushing the cup along the ground!

2. You can steal food from another student if he/she is still trying to get it into his/her mouth (cup). Food in the cup that has been "eaten" already cannot be stolen.

STEP 5. After the stop signal is given, count the number of beans and worms you have collected. Each bean or worm is assigned a food value. The camouflaged seeds and the worms are harder to find, so they will be given a food value of two, and the more visible seeds are given a value of one. Enter the beak phenotype of your group and the number of each type of food in Table 8.5 on the bottom of this page. Figure 8.3 directly below is an example of how to complete the table.

**Figure 8.3 Type and number of prey caught by the first generation**

| bird phenotype:<br><br>*drinking straw* | visible beans | camouflaged beans | worms | |
|---|---|---|---|---|
| number of food item caught | 20 | 5 | 5 | |
| value of food item | 1 | 2 | 2 | |
| no. of food items X food value | 20 | 10 | 10 | total<br><br>40 |

**Table 8.5 Type and number of prey caught by the first generation**

| bird phenotype: | visible beans | camouflaged beans | worms | |
|---|---|---|---|---|
| number of food item caught | | | | |
| value of food item | 1 | 2 | 2 | |
| no. of food items X food value | | | | total |

STEP 6. The total number of offspring will be equal to the total food value. Provide the number for your beak type to the instructor for tabulation of Table 8.6.

The instructor will summarize the class values to enter into Table 8.6. The total percent of offspring of each beak phenotype will be calculated to determine the number of students that will represent the phenotype in the next generation.

**Table 8.6 Type and number of prey caught by the first generation by bird phenotype**

|  | drinking straw | pencils | tweezers | clothes-pin | stick | spoon | totals |
|---|---|---|---|---|---|---|---|
| total off-spring |  |  |  |  |  |  |  |
| % total off-spring |  |  |  |  |  |  |  |
| no. of birds in the next generation |  |  |  |  |  |  |  |

STEP 7. Repeat the hunt three more times. Summarize the class data for the number of birds in all phenotypes participating in the hunt for food throughout five generations by completing Tables 8.7 – 8.12 on the following pages.

**Table 8.7 Type and number of prey caught by the second generation**

| bird phenotype: | visible beans | camouflaged beans | worms | |
|---|---|---|---|---|
| number of food item caught | | | | |
| value of food item | 1 | 2 | 2 | |
| no. of food items X food value | | | | total |

The instructor will summarize the class values to enter into Table 8.8. The total percent of offspring of each beak phenotype will be calculated to determine the number of students that will represent the phenotype in the next generation.

**Table 8.8 Type and number of prey caught by the second generation by bird phenotype**

| | drinking straw | pencils | tweezers | clothes-pin | stick | spoon | totals |
|---|---|---|---|---|---|---|---|
| total off-spring | | | | | | | |
| % total off-spring | | | | | | | |
| no. of birds in the next generation | | | | | | | |

**Table 8.9 Type and number of prey caught by the third generation**

| bird phenotype: | visible beans | camouflaged beans | worms | |
|---|---|---|---|---|
| number of food item caught | | | | |
| value of food item | 1 | 2 | 2 | |
| no. of food items X food value | | | | total |

The instructor will summarize the class values to enter into Table 8.10. The total percent of offspring of each beak phenotype will be calculated to determine the number of students that will represent the phenotype in the next generation.

**Table 8.10 Type and number of prey caught by the third generation by bird phenotype**

| | drinking straw | pencils | tweezers | clothes-pin | stick | spoon | totals |
|---|---|---|---|---|---|---|---|
| total off-spring | | | | | | | |
| % total off-spring | | | | | | | |
| no. of birds in the next generation | | | | | | | |

**Table 8.11 Type and number of prey caught by the fourth generation**

| bird phenotype: | visible beans | camouflaged beans | worms | |
|---|---|---|---|---|
| number of food item caught | | | | |
| value of food item | 1 | 2 | 2 | |
| no. of food items X food value | | | | total |

The instructor will summarize the class values to enter into Table 8.12. The total percent of offspring of each beak phenotype will be calculated to determine the number of students that will represent the phenotype in the next generation.

**Table 8.12 Type and number of prey caught by the fourth generation by bird phenotype**

| | drinking straw | pencils | tweezers | clothes-pin | stick | spoon | totals |
|---|---|---|---|---|---|---|---|
| total off-spring | | | | | | | |
| % total off-spring | | | | | | | |
| no. of birds in the next generation | | | | | | | |

STEP 8. Use the class summaries of each generation from Tables 8.8, 8.10, and 8.12 to complete Table 8.13 below. The first column is the number of birds in the initial generation.

**Table 8.13 The number of birds in each beak phenotype by generation**

| bird phenotype | Number of birds per generation | | | | |
|---|---|---|---|---|---|
| | 1 | 2 | 3 | 4 | 5 |
| drinking-straw shaped | | | | | |
| pencil shaped | | | | | |
| tweezer shaped | | | | | |
| clothespin shaped | | | | | |
| stick shaped | | | | | |
| spoon shaped | | | | | |
| totals | | | | | |

STEP 9. Graph the results of the hunt with the data from Table 8.13. Graph paper is located at the end of this lab. See also Appendix H, preparing a simple graph. Overlay the results for each bird phenotype by using different symbols for each phenotype. The independent variable will be the generation number.

17. Over time, what happened to the size of the population as a whole?

*decreased*

18. What happened to the overall genetic variation in the population?

*Variation went down*

19. Did your beak phenotype thrive or die out? Why?

*thrive*

20. How did your predictions about beak phenotype success compare to the results? Explain.

21. How do the different food types affect individual survival?

    Certain foods are not compatible, those with the best type will survive

22. Were there other factors besides beak shape that seemed to be important in survival? Explain.

    ambition, aggressive, modification

23. In the big picture, what determines how many birds having a particular beak shape will be in the next generation?

    how much food they get.

24. Within this population of birds was an extraordinary individual. He was born with a stick shaped beak, but after months and months of rubbing his beak on a smooth rock, he was able to flatten and broaden the end so it looked a little bit like a spoon. This allowed him to be a little more successful at eating beans. Would you expect his offspring to have a beak that is a little more spoon shaped like his? Why or why not?

    no, it's not inherited

**SUMMARY QUESTION**

Explain how natural selection controls the genetic diversity found in populations. One member of your group may be asked to share this with the class during discussion.

**POST-LAB QUESTIONS**                    Name _____

1.  What might be an advantage to having a phenotype in the middle of the range in a population?

2.  What does the whole class with different bird beaks represent?

3.  What determines how many baby birds will be born having a certain beak shape?

4.  Did evolution occur in an individual or in the population? Explain your answer.

5.  Imagine that changes in the environment made it so that only worms remained. Predict how this might change the percentages of bird beak phenotypes seen in the population after five generations. Would these results differ from the results we got in this demonstration? Why or why not?

*Questions continue on the next page.*

6. What other factors, beyond genetics, could possibly explain the type of variation in a population?

7. Were there selective pressures on the prey items of the bird beak activity? Explain.

8. Predict what might happen to the genetic variation of the population of beans if the instructor did not replace them for each new generation.

9. Some people have lasix surgery to improve their vision. Is there an advantage to the individual, the population, or the species if an individual modifies its phenotype?

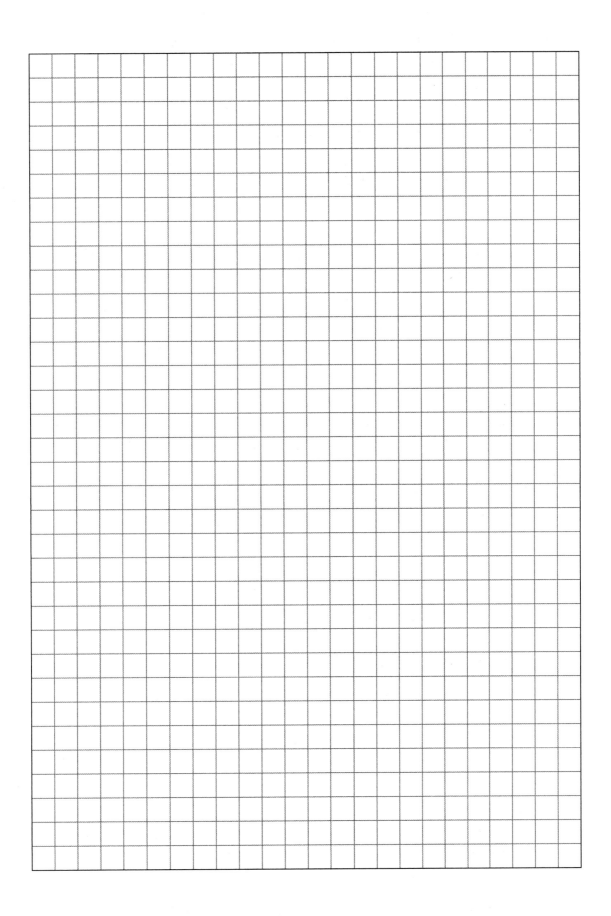

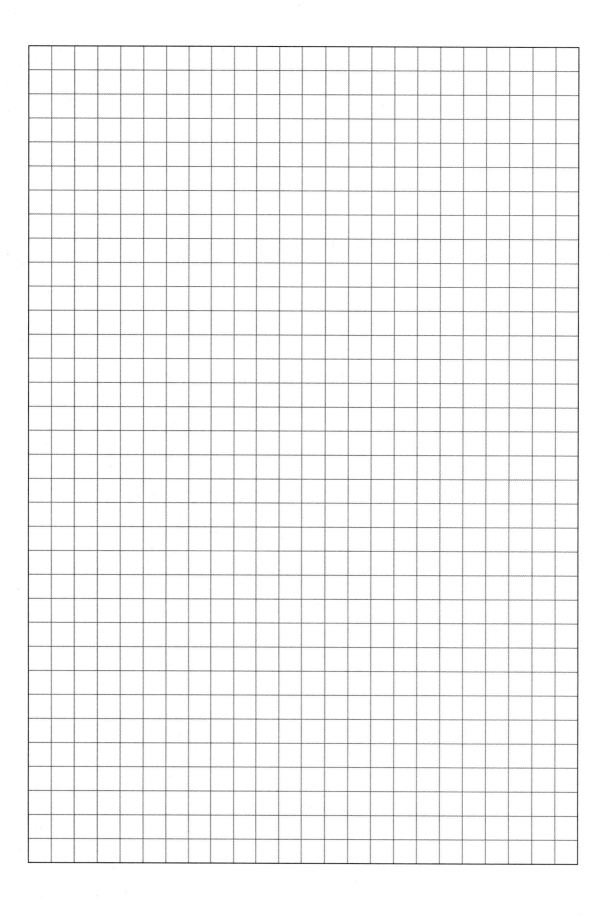

# SYSTEMATICS

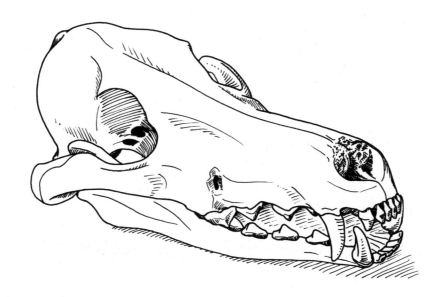

How do we organize all the species on Earth?  What relationships exist among species? What are the tools that are used to establish ancestry? How do biologists group similar species? These questions will form the framework for your activities in today's lab.

How do we organize all the species on Earth?  You learned that all organisms on Earth use a common DNA-protein code to determine which protein products the cell makes. The products made by the cells affect the traits of the organism and these traits are used to organize species.  Members of all three domains (Bacteria, Archaea, and Eukarya) use the same code, yet can be significantly different in their final appearance.  Sharing the same code is evidence of the shared ancestry of all species.  Over time, changes in the descendents of earlier species have accumulated leading to the diversity we see today.

What relationships exist among species? Cellular products that impact critical life functions are more likely to be conserved with little change over time. However, over long time periods, random minor changes in the DNA will accumulate to significant amounts. Biologists deduce that if species A and species B have fewer differences in a critical protein than the differences in that protein between species B and C, then species B is likely to be more closely related to species A than species C. We can become more certain of these relationships by comparing other traits found in species A, B, and C.

What are the tools that are used to establish ancestry? **Fossils** are the remains or evidence of past organisms. Fossils are useful to compare differences of form among species. **Paleobiologists** are biologists who study fossils. Paleobiologists gain additional evidence about the relative age of species by their location in geological strata; older species are buried deeper. Biologists are interested in determining the older, ancestral species in order to understand evolutionary development.

How do biologists group similar species? **Systematics** is the process and study of sorting. Systematics includes three main areas of study, (1) description of species, (2) naming of species, and (3) the evolutionary history of a species. The description includes a listing of key distinctive traits.  The naming system used is called **taxonomy**. A **taxon** is a group of similar species. Biologists use a hierarchy of taxa to organize groups of living things, starting with the broadest and most inclusive taxon, the domain. The taxa get more and more exclusive further "down" the hierarchy and eventually name an organism by it genus and species epithet. (See Appendix G for the hierarchical listing.) This greatly helps us in discussing the over 10 million species alive today! The evolutionary history of a species is called its **phylogeny**.

**PRE-LAB QUESTIONS**                    **Name** _____

1. What evidence is there that all life on Earth is related?




2. Describe methods that are used to distinguish between species and sort them into groups.




3. How is phylogeny related to systematics?

## STUDENT LEARNING OUTCOMES

Upon completion of today's lab, you will be able to do the following:

    I.   explain how molecular markers could be used to establish phylogenies,

    II.  explore how skull morphology could be used to understand an animal's ecological niche, and

    III. classify organisms using dichotomous keys.

## I. USING MOLECULAR MARKERS

There are multiple ways to compare similarities and differences among species. Biologists can observe how the organism functions or appears. With respect to using function as a way to sort, consider that a tree may be distinguished from your pet cat because it gets its energy from the sun, not by eating. Sorting coyotes and wolves together as a group makes sense because they appear distinct from lions and leopards. Sorting by appearance can be done at the microscopic level as well; you recall that the first separation of organisms into domains was determined by the presence or absence of a nuclear membrane.

Information on the phylogeny of a species can be gained by comparing key areas of its genome with that of a similar species. Biologists use nucleases that cut at specific base pair locations in the DNA of particular chromosomes within those key areas. Cut fragments of DNA may then be compared for size. If similar-sized fragments of DNA are found in two species and not in other species, those fragments of DNA are evidence those two species are more closely related. DNA fragment differences may also identify new developments. An additional fragment in one of the species may indicate the addition of a new gene. A new gene suggests that it is the more recent species.

In this activity, you will be working with simulated fragments of DNA taken from the same area of the genome of five different animals. All five animals will have some DNA in common, and some will have DNA that is common with only one or two others, and some may have novel or new fragments of DNA. By separating the fragments into common sizes and colors, you should be able to solve our phylogenetic puzzle.

You will use electrophoresis equipment that separates molecules by both their weight and charge. In lab 3, "Movement across the plasma membrane", you saw that through diffusion you could separate molecules by weight. Electrophoresis separates molecules by weight and also uses an electrical current to help pull the samples through the gel. Molecules that are negatively charged are pulled to the positive charge on one side of the gel tray, and molecules that are positively charged are drawn to the negatively charged side of the gel tray. DNA molecules have a negative charge. Samples containing simulated DNA will be placed at one end of a flat gel, and over time, the different fragments will separate. There are three parts to this procedure, with some waiting time in between. During the waiting periods, you should begin working on activities II and III of this lab.

### I. A. Casting a gel

**Materials**

      on your lab bench
           electrophoresis apparatus with casting tray and power supply
           agarose
           metal scoop
           scale
           weigh boat
           100 mL graduated cylinder
           250 mL Erlenmeyer flask
           hot plate
           red hot mitt
           stir bar
           magnetic wand

      on instructor's bench
           0.5% TAE buffer solution in carboy

**Procedure**

STEP 1.  Take the 100 mL graduated cylinder from your lab bench and go to the carboy on the instructor's bench to measure 65 mL of TAE buffer.  Return to your lab bench and pour the 65 mL of buffer solution to the 250 mL Erlenmeyer flask.

STEP 2. Use the metal scoop to transfer and measure 0.52 g of agarose on a weigh boat, then add the agarose to the buffer solution in the 250 mL Erlenmeyer flask.

STEP 3.  Gently mix the agarose with the buffer by swirling the Erlenmeyer flask.

STEP 4. *Read* steps 5-9 first before your proceed with step 5.

STEP 5. Place a stir bar in the Erlenmeyer flask, and then place the flask on the hot plate. Turn on the hot plate to 300° and turn the stir setting to 200 rpm. ***Do not leave the solution unattended.***

STEP 6. Keep the solution on the hot plate for about *five minutes* until it is clear. Turn down the stir setting if you see any bubbles form. ***You do not want bubbles.*** *Be careful not to let it clump or burn.  If the solution starts to boil, use the hot gloves to remove the flask from the hot plate.*

STEP 7. Once the solution is clear and comes just to boiling, use the red hot mitt to remove it from the hot plate immediately. *Remove the stir bar* with the magnetic wand. Turn off the hot plate.

STEP 8.  Allow the solution to cool on the lab bench for approximately 15 minutes, or until it cools enough to touch the flask; the flask will still be warm. While it is cooling, set up the casting tray. *Do not swirl to check the temperature. Move the solution gently so as not to create surface bubbles. The solution should cool enough to touch but still be warm.*

STEP 9. To set up the casting tray at your lab bench, close off the open ends of the casting tray with the rubber dams. Please see Figure 9.1 below. Insert the comb into the first notch of the negative side. The tab is located on the negative side.

**Figure 9.1 Electrophoresis gel tray with dams**

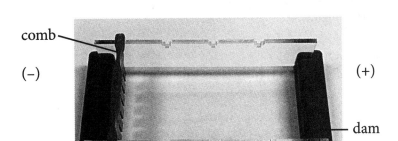

STEP 10. To cast the cooled gel, *the casting tray must be on a flat surface.* Gently holding down the comb, slowly and without interuption pour the clear gel solution into the casting tray. The comb will create wells for your samples. Wait until the gel solidifies, turning translucent, before proceeding. The gel will solidify in about 20 minutes. It will not be clear. *Do not continue with I.B. until the gel has solidified.*

Proceed to Section II, the skull analysis, while the gels are cooling. Then return to activity I. B.

## I. B. Loading samples and running the gel

### Materials

on your lab bench
> electrophoresis apparatus with casting tray and power supply
> micropipetters and tips
> practice pipetting plate
> waste container for used micropipette tips
> practice dye solution
> "DNA" test samples for species A, B, C, D, and E in microcentrifuge tubes
> 500 mL graduated cylinder
> practice plate

on instructor's bench
> 0.5% TAE buffer solution in carboy
> used buffer container

### Procedure

STEP 1. Carefully remove the comb by lifting straight up.

STEP 2. Carefully remove the rubber dams from the gel tray.

STEP 3. Put a sheet of white paper underneath the electrophoresis chamber. Place the gel tray in the electrophoresis chamber so that the wells created by the comb are oriented near the negative electrode (black). Please see Figure 9.2 below.

### Figure 9.2 Gel tray in electrophoresis apparatus

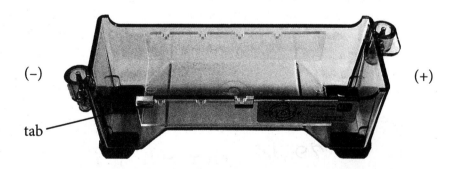

STEP 4. Take your 500 mL graduated cylinder to the side counter and measure out 300 mL of TAE buffer solution. Return to your lab bench and gently pour the 300 mL of TAE buffer solution at one side of the electrophoresis chamber, adjacent to the gel tray. The buffer solution should completely submerge your gel.

STEP 5. Practice using the micropipetter: add a small amount of water to the practice plate. Put a tip on the micropipetter. Place your thumb on the plunger and gently depress the plunger to the first stop and place the micropipetter in the practice dye solution. Keeping your thumb on the plunger, release the pressure slowly to withdraw dye. *Without removing your thumb*, lift the micropipetter out of the solution, move it under the water but still over a well of the practice plate. *The tip should be just above the well but under the water.* Press to the second stop to dispense the liquid. **Keep your thumb on the plunger until you remove the micropipetter from the liquid.** Press on the separate ejection button to release the pipette tip into the waste container. When finished practicing pipetting, rinse off the practice plate and leave it on your table to dry.

STEP 6. Using the micropipetter, slowly and gently dispense 15.0 μL of each species' test sample from the microcentrifuge tubes into the appropriate sample well made by the comb by following the testing scheme below.  Be sure to use a new tip for each sample.

*When loading the dye into buffer, submerge the tip just above the well in the gel and under the liquid.*

Use the following scheme:
　　　　well 1　　　　　species A
　　　　well 2　　　　　species B
　　　　well 3　　　　　species C
　　　　well 4　　　　　species D
　　　　well 5　　　　　species E

STEP 7. Put the cover on the chamber, plug in the power lines (red to red and black to black), and turn on the power supply to 150V. The gel electrophoresis apparatus is shown in Figure 9.3 below. It will take approximately 60 minutes to complete the run. The gel should be stopped when the first color comes close to the end of the plate. When this happens, turn off the power supply.

**Figure 9.3  Gel electrophoresis apparatus**

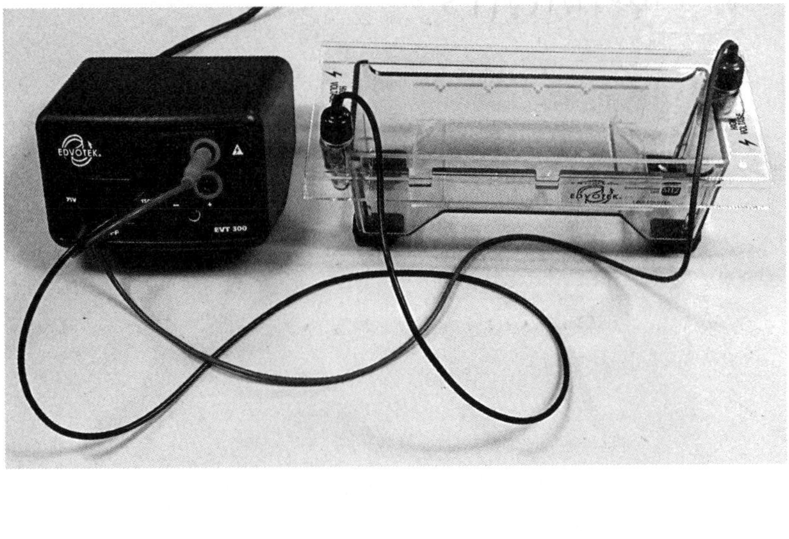

STEP 8. Proceed to Section III while the samples are running, and keep an eye on the color separations on the gel.

**Figure 9.4 Sample electrophoresis gel**

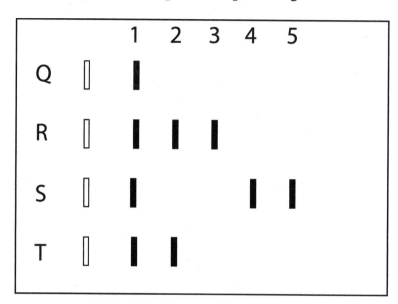

The sample electrophoresis gel, Figure 9.4 above, shows the separation of DNA from four different animal species: Q, R, S, and T. All species share a fragment of the same size, indicated by the position labeled "1." This is the only fragment identified from species Q, so species Q is most likely the earliest species. Species R and T share two fragments, at positions "1" and "2", suggesting they are more closely related to each other than they are to species S. Since species R has one more DNA fragment at position "3" than species T, species T probably is older than species R.

1. Each dye solution represents a "sample" taken from five different animal species. What molecule is represented in each sample?

   *DNA fragments*

2. What do the different bands on the gel show?

   *They represent DNA of different sizes.*

3. Why are there so many bands per species?

   *different animals has different DNA.*

4. Which color dye has the smallest molecule? How do you know?

*Yellow - furthest to the top*

5. What does it mean if two species have a band in common?

*They have the same DNA fragments.*

6. Which color dye represents a molecule shared by all the test animals?

*yellow/orange - all of them have it so it must be important.*

7. Which animal is most different from the others?  Explain your answer.

*C*

8. Which species may be younger than species D? Explain your answer.

9. Based on your data, which species seems to be most closely related to species E? Explain your answer.

10. Challenge question.  If these five samples represent *Tyrannosaurus rex*, a duck, a frog, a cat, and a wolf, can you match the sample to the animal?

    species A _____

    species B _____

    species C _____

    species D _____

    species E _____

STEP 9.  Pour the buffer solution used in the electrophoresis apparatus in the used buffer container on the instructor's bench.

STEP 10. Dispose of your used gels in the trash.  Carefully clean all glassware and all other materials used and return to their original places.

STEP 11. DRAW your results in the figure below.

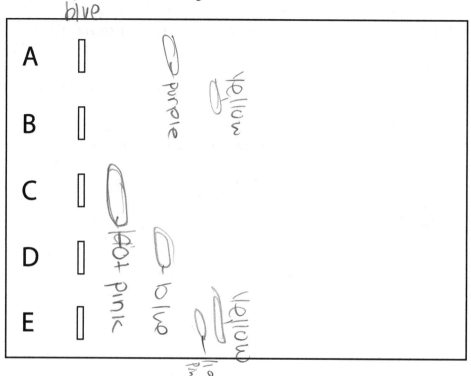

11. In your own words, summarize how this experiment separating simulated DNA molecules from different species helped you determine how the five species were related to each other.

The matching colors help determine who the match is.

## II. GETTING CLUES FROM MORPHOLOGY

Bones are designed to work with muscles to move joints. Where a muscle attaches to a bone there is a rough area or bump due to the pull of the muscle on the bone. A larger area for muscle attachment indicates that more muscle was attached in that location. More muscle may create a stronger movement than a similarly sized bone with a smaller muscle attached. In addition, because the bones are being used as levers, the length of the bone provides an indication of the range of motion and potentially the speed of motion that occurs at a joint when the muscle contracts.

Comparison of skull anatomy has been fundamental in vertebrate systematics. Through natural selection, bones have evolved to reflect different functions. For example, in mammals, the **teeth** and **jaws** provide a great deal of information about what that species eats. Mammals have four possible distinctive teeth types: incisors, canine, premolars, and molars. Incisors cut, canines rip and tear, and molars are used to grind food. Mammals use their teeth to cut their food into smaller bits and chew it. The teeth of fish and reptiles are all about the same size and shape and are generally good only for gripping prey. See Figures 9.5 and 9.6 below and on the next page for a comparison between the skulls of a mammal and a reptile.

**Figure 9.5 The skull of a reptile**

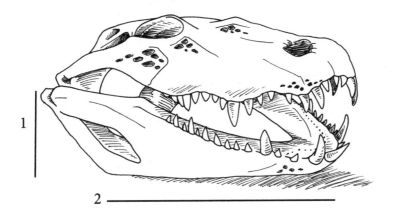

(1) ramus   (2) lower jaw

**Figure 9.6 The skull of a mammal**

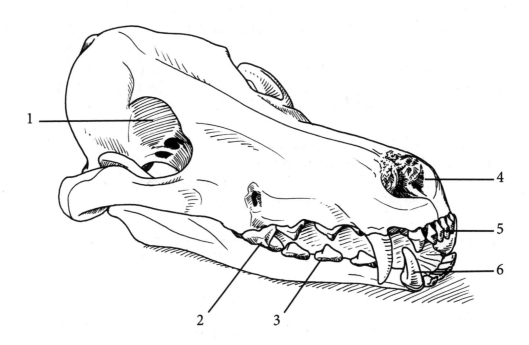

(1) orbit  (2) molar  (3) premolar  (4) nasal cavity  (5) incisor  (6) canine

The relative positions of different structures also provide clues about the animals. For example, animals with **eyes** placed on either side of their heads are able to view a wide field. Those animals are generally herbivores and prey for carnivores. Animals with two forward-facing eyes gain stereoscopic vision because the fields of view overlap. Animals with stereoscopic vision make good hunters. The eyes of vertebrates are located inside a special cavity called the **orbit**.

In this exercise, you will examine 12 vertebrate skulls. Your observations will help you formulate hypotheses regarding adaptations of structures seen in the different taxa of vertebrates.

**Materials**

      on side counter

          stations 1-6

               two skulls per station

               appropriate measuring equipment

               pipe cleaners to use for pointing or touching skulls

**Procedure**

STEP 1. Proceed to station 1. Consider the sense of sight in these animals.  Eyes are located in the orbits.

12.  Measure the diameter of an orbit in each skull.

species A ___24___ cm

species B ___16___ cm

13.  Hypothesize on the relative importance of sight based on the size of the orbit relative to head size or other senses.

B has bigger eye sockets – site is important

14.  Hypothesize if the species are herbivores or carnivores based on their eye positioning. Explain your answer.

A is herbivore – eyes on the side
B is Carnivore

15.  Make additional observations about these two skulls.

A is huge –

STEP 2.  Proceed to station 2. Consider the teeth and jaws in these animals. The **ramus** is the vertical section of the jaw next to the joint. See also Figure 9.4.

16.  Measure the length and ramus of the lower jaw in each species.

species C      ramus ___60___ cm      length of jaw ___26___ cm

species D      ramus ___35___ cm      length of jaw ___18___ cm

STEP 3. After measuring the depth of the ramus and the length of the mandible calculate the ratio of the ramus to the length of the jaw.

species C ___60:26___        species D ___35:18___

17.  Which species has a larger ramus/length ratio?

D alligator – much larger
more room for muscle,

18. What does this ratio tell us about the possible biting force of each animal?

    *C bigger biting strength. - Beaver*

19. What differences are there between the teeth shapes of these two animals.

    *D has larger teeth but flat*
    *C has sharp teeth*

20. Based on the jaw and teeth, which animal skull would be better suited for chewing or grinding hard materials and which would be better suited for grasping and tearing larger items?

    *D → chewing /grinding*
    *C → grasping / tearing*

21. Make additional observations about these two skulls.

    *C has a flatter skull*

STEP 4.   Proceed to station 3. Consider adaptations in the skull relative to habitat.

22. Do you think that these animals are aquatic/semi-aquatic or terrestrial? Explain your answer.

    *Semiaquatic texture of skull*

23. Why do you think species F's eye orbits (and nostrils?) are on the top of it's head?

    *to see, breathe above water.*

24. Hypothesize about how species E and F can stealthily capture their prey.

    *sneak up under water*

25. Make additional observations about these two skulls.

STEP 5. Proceed to station 4. Consider the relative dimensions of the craniums in these animals and how that affects their diet.

26. Look at the jaws on these animals! How do they chew?

    *not well - do not chew.*

27. Guess which one is the hunter. What senses are used to locate their prey? Explain your answer.

    *G has eyes in front, he is the hunter*

28. Measure the cranium circumference at the widest part and the length of the skull, including beak.

    species G
    cranium circumference ___21___ cm

    length of skull ___10___ cm
    species H
    cranium circumference ___19___ cm

    length of skull ___14___ cm

29. Compare the ratio of cranium to skull length.

    species G
    cranium height/length of skull:    *4:10*

    species H
    cranium height/length of skull:

    *4.5:14*

30. Which species has the larger cranium circumference/ length ratio?  Why do you think this animal has the larger ratio?

4  Tle owl huge visual center.

31. Make additional observations about these two skulls.

STEP 6. Proceed to station 5. These skulls are both from the same class of vertebrates. Because they share a common ancestry, the ancestor's bones were modified and adapted for different purposes.  Look for cavities, holes, and ridges on these skulls.  Cavities like the orbits may hold organs.  Blood vessels and nerves pass through holes. Ridges may be sites for muscle attachment.

32. What common cavities are seen in these two skulls?

The eyes on top of head, Tle nose.

33. What are the bumps on the bone used for? Which species has larger bumps?

Where tle muscle attach, J has bigger bumps.

34. How are the hinges for the jaws different?  Hypothesize which species has a stronger jaw.

One is more flat, J has a stronger Jaw

35. What are the differences in how these animals may grab their food?

J snaps down on food, tle second one has sharp teeth to snap it off

36.  Make additional observations about these two skulls.

STEP 7.  Proceed to station 6. These animals are both mammals so they have differentiated teeth.

37.  What do these skulls have in common?

Sharp teeth - Coyote, pointy teeth.
eyes on front - cat

38.  Count the different teeth types on these mammals.

4 fangs                    6-12 back teeth
12 Short front teeth

39.  Are these animals predators or prey?  Explain why you think so.

Predators based on teeth + eyes

40.  Speculate on the size of their respective food sources.

food Source - meat

41.  Make additional observations about these two skulls.

Smaller Skulls are more round than long

42.  What do you think is the most useful skull feature to sort animals? Explain your answer.

teeth are most usefull to eat more
Prospecks

43. Summarize how examining a skull can provide insight into an animal's habitat and diet.

teeth - determine what type of food
eyes - eyes determine hunting prey
Jaw - if contains muscle it will
have a strong bite.

## III. WORKING WITH DICHOTOMOUS KEYS

Biologists have another way to sort the millions of species on Earth. The premise is simple: when you look at an organism, it either has a trait or it does not. This is sorting by **dichotomy**. Sorting organisms is as easy as going through a list of traits to see if your organism has the trait or not. For you to understand how this works, you will sort 10 insects. Biologists put the sorting guide into procedures called **keys** and use the keys in the field to identify species. By separating in a dichotomous fashion, biologists can quickly indentify a species. Figure 9.7 below provides an example of a simple dichotomous key.

**Figure 9.7 Example of a dichotomous sorting key for five mammals: gorilla, deer, mouse, cat, bat**

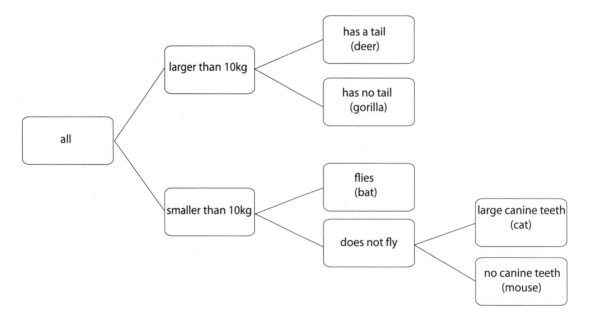

**Materials**

    on side counter
        insect identification chart

    on your lab bench
        box with 10 plastimount insect specimens, labeled 1-10
        ruler

**Procedure**

STEP 1.  Open the box of insects, and remove the plastimount insect specimens. *Please be careful not to drop or scratch the specimens!* Your specimens are labeled 1-10 for ease of use.

STEP 2.  Figure 9.8 below illustrates some features seen in insets. On the side counter you will find an insect identification chart with additional insect features. After studying this information, separate the insects based on the presence or absence of a trait into two new subgroups.

**Figure 9.8 Diagram of insect structures**

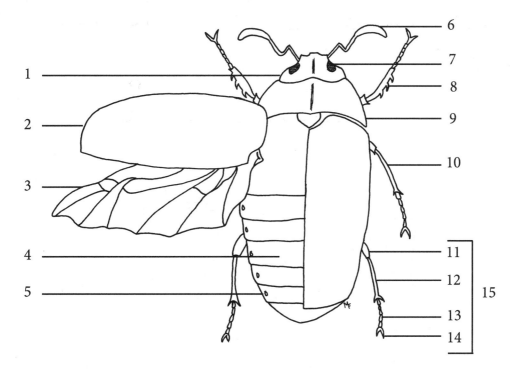

| | | |
|---|---|---|
| (1) head | (6) antenna | (11) femur |
| (2) front wing | (7) compound eye | (12) tibia |
| (3) hind wing | (8) front leg | (13) tarsus |
| (4) abdominal segment | (9) thorax | (14) claws |
| (5) spiracle | (10) middle leg | (15) hind leg |

STEP 3. Use Figure 9.9 below as a sorting template to continue sorting the insects and prepare your own dichotomous key. Sort the specimens into two groups based on one trait that is found in some of the species, but not others. In addition to the traits depicted on the diagram or chart, you may consider descriptive traits based on color, size, or structure.

**Figure 9.9 How to set up a dichotomous key**

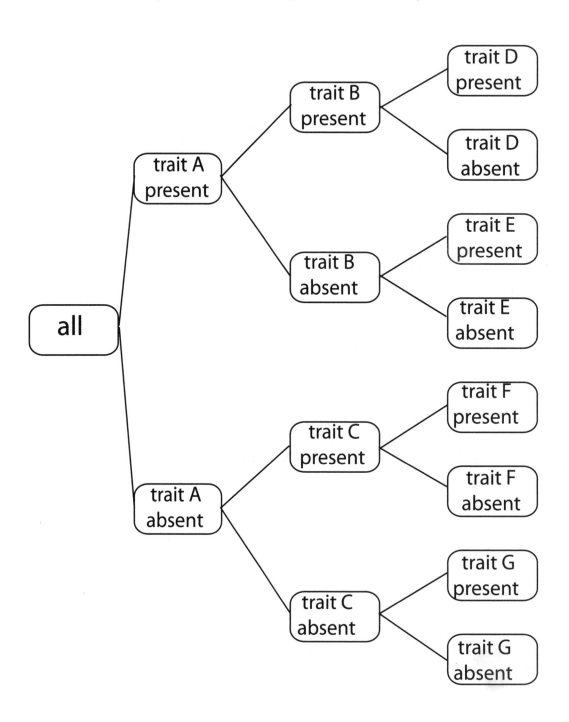

STEP 4.  With one of your two groups, identify a trait that is found in one or more, but not all of the insects in that group. Separate the insects based on that trait into two new subgroups and add that trait to your key.

STEP 5. Continue separating the insects based on their traits until each one stands alone and apart from the others because of their unique combination of traits.

44.  Write your dichotomous key here.

1  Stag beetle

2  Striped beetle

3  Wasp

4  green tiger beetle

5  Cicada

6  long horn beetle

7  honey bee

8  bamboo weevil

9  Chafer beetle

10  Cockroach

45. Your instructor will check your sorting guide and initial your lab book here.

   Instructor initials _____

STEP 6.   Obtain a sample insect and a dichotomous key from your instructor. Use it to determine the name of the insect.

46. List the traits of your test insect that distinguish it from all the other insects here and identify the name of the test insect.

47. What part of the scientific method did you use while making the dichotomous key?

48. Why did you make a sorting guide and how is that related to a dichotomous key?

**SUMMARY QUESTION**

Prepare a statement summarizing and describing all the different methods you learned to organize and sort animals.  One member of your lab group should be prepared to share this with the rest of the class at the end of the day.

**POST-LAB QUESTIONS**                                 Name _____

1.  Why were the DNA-simulated samples put near the negative electrode?

2.  How is DNA related to traits?

3.  What can you learn about an animal by studying its bones / skulls?

4.  Which species do you suspect has a good sense of smell by their skull structure? Explain.

5.  Explain how using a dichotomous key can make sorting species easier.

6.  Of the three methods in systematics you learned today, which method(s) would you use to sort fossils of extinct species? Explain your choice.

# ANIMALS, PART ONE

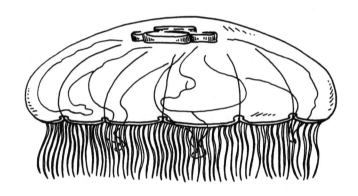

What traits do all animals share? How do animals get their nutrition and energy? How do we sort animals? What can we use to understand and observe animals more closely? These questions will form the framework for your activities in today's lab.

What traits do all animals share? The kingdom of animals is in the domain Eukarya, so all members of this kingdom have cells with a membrane-bound nucleus. A single-celled organism is limited in its potential size and complexity; animals are multi-cellular organisms that can exhibit both large size and complexity. Cell division in animals occurs by mitosis for repair and growth, and by meiosis to produce gametes. Animals are diploid, and most reproduce sexually. Most animals have cells organized into more complex layers that share a specific structure and function, called **tissues**. Examples of tissue types in animals include surface-covering tissues, internal tissues that connect and support body parts, and two tissues to sense and respond to their environment.

How do animals get their nutrition and energy? Animals are **heterotrophic**, which means they obtain their energy by consuming other organisms, in contrast to **autotrophic** organisms like plants that produce their own food. Animals move when searching for food.

How do we sort animals? Biologists organize the phyla of the large animal kingdom by various criteria. The first criterion is to determine if an animal has true **tissues**. The second way to sort animals is by whether they have two or three embryonic **germ tissue layers**. A germ tissue layer is the first level of cellular organization that will give rise to different structures of the body. Please see also Appendix G for the organization of selected animal phyla.

As the animal kingdom expanded in size, the design of some animals became more complex and organized, enabling them to go into different habitats and use different food sources. Some useful traits, such as having sensory organs concentrated at one end of the body, or segmented body parts, arose in multiple phyla. However, each animal phylum also has unique traits. Using both general descriptors of the body design and the unique traits of a phylum is critical to the classification of animals.

What can we use to understand and observe animals more closely? Some animals, although multi-cellular, are microscopic, and so we need to use a compound light microscope to observe them. Other animals are large enough to see with the naked eye, but have small structural details that are more easily observed using a **dissecting** microscope.

**PRE-LAB QUESTIONS**                    Name _____

1.  Describe at least three traits that all animals share.

2.  You are an animal. Give two specific examples of how muscle and/or nervous tissue help you in your heterotrophic lifestyle.

**STUDENT LEARNING OUTCOMES**

Upon completion of today's lab, you will be able to do the following:

I. describe the general characteristics of animals,
II. describe adaptations in body plan and unique traits of major animal phyla, and
III. use a dissecting microscope.

Specific changes in the designs of body plans included variations of body symmetry, digestive systems, nervous systems, structural support systems, means of locomotion, and the development of a head (cephalization), and segmentation. Different designs of body plans can help us sort animals into groups.

## I. GENERAL CHARACTERISTICS OF THE PHYLUM PORIFERA

The phylum **Porifera** includes sponges. Most sponges live in the ocean, but a few species live in freshwater. Sponges are the simplest animals. Adults are **sessile** and attach to rocks or other objects, but larvae are ciliated and mobile.

Animals in the phylum Porifera do not have true tissues. This criterion separates Porifera from the other animal phyla you are examining. Two major cell types found in sponges include flagellated **choanocytes**, also know as collar cells, and **amoebocytes**. The choanocytes line pores leading into the sponge, and the movement of the flagella of the choanocytes moves water through the pores. The amoebocytes make a basic support system called **spicules** of chalk (calcium carbonate), glass (silica), or spongin (fibrous protein). Water flows into a central cavity, the **spongocoel**, and then out the exit hole, the **osculum**. The cells of the sponges phagocytize small particles in the water current. Sponges are considered **filter feeders** because of this trait.

1. How does the information in the above paragraph provide support for the statement that sponges are animals?

   *The sponges are multicellular, They reproduce and Eukaryotic.*

**Materials**

on side counter

Porifera display including

Porifera chart and representative classes
sponge specimens labeled (1) and (2)
preserved specimens of *Grantia* sp.
watch glass
forceps
bottle of water

on your lab bench

blunt metal probe
prepared slide of *Grantia* sp. (cs and ls)
prepared slide whole mount of sponge showing spicules (wm)
compound light microscope

**Procedure**

STEP 1. Go to the side counter Porifera display to obtain a specimen of the sponge *Grantia* sp. Put enough culture water to cover the bottom of a watch glass, and use the forceps to extract a specimen from the specimen bottle.

STEP 2. Using two hands, carry a dissecting microscope from the front cabinet to your lab bench. Plug it in, and turn on the light switch found at the back of the base.

STEP 3. Place the watch glass with your specimen on the center of the base of the dissecting microscope. The black knob is the focus knob, and the white knob is the magnifying knob. Check that the magnification is set at the lowest setting, 8.

STEP 4. Turn on the lamp by pressing the light bulb icon found on the base. Then, starting with the nosepiece in the lowest position and with your hand on the focus knob, look into the ocular lenses. Gradually rotate the focus knob until the specimen comes into clear focus. Use the blunt probe to poke at the specimen (*do not tear it!*) to see how water moves throughout the sponge.

2. LABEL the choanocyte, amoebocytes spicule, pores and osculum on the sponge in Figure 10.1 on the next page.

**Figure 10.1 A sponge**

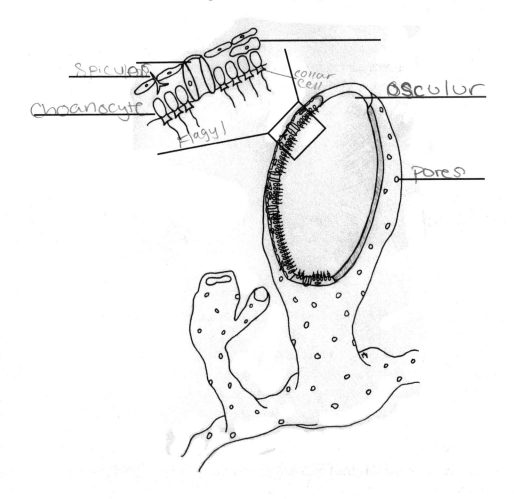

Labels on figure: Spicule, Choanocyte, Flagyl, collar cell, oscUlur, pores

STEP 5. Return your sponge specimen to the jar on the side counter. Clean and return the watch glass.

STEP 6. On the side counter, look at the sponge specimens labeled (1) and (2). These specimens are no longer living; only the support structures remain.

3.  Did specimen (1) have a support structure made of chalk, glass, or spongin?

    Specimen 1 is made up of spicules

4.  Did specimen (2) have a support structure made of chalk, glass, or spongin?

    specimen is made up of spongin.

STEP 7. Observe the prepared slide of the whole mount (wm) of the sponge on your compound light microscope.

  5.  What are the sharp extensions seen on the sponge?

      *Spicules*

STEP 8. Observe the prepared slide of the cross section (cs) of the sponge, *Grantia* sp. on your compound light microscope.

  6.  What is the function of the cells lining the spaces?

      *Move water and trap it.*

## II. GENERAL CHARACTERISTICS OF THE PHYLUM CNIDARIA

Members of the animal phylum **Cnidaria** demonstrate an increase in the complexity of the body plan when compared to Porifera. Members of this phylum have symmetry, distinct digestive systems, nervous tissue, and muscle fibers. A unique trait in this phylum is stinging cells that cnidarians discharge from their tentacles to numb their prey.

The phylum Cnidaria is different from other animal phyla with true tissues because they only have two germ tissue layers; the other animal phyla we are studying have three germ tissue layers.

**Materials**

  on side counter

    Cnidaria display including

      Cnidaria chart and representative classes
      *Hydra* sp. live specimens
      water fleas (*Daphnia* sp.) to feed *Hydra* sp.
      depression slides
      disposable pipettes to transfer specimens
      prepared slides of *Hydra* sp.
      specimen jars with representative cnidarians

  on your lab bench

    insect pin
    disposable pipette
    compound light microscope

**Procedure**

STEP 1. Observe the display showing the diversity of the phylum Cnidaria. There are two general body forms, a **polyp**, with tentacles extending upward, and a **medusa** form, with the tentacles hanging down. The polyp form attaches to a substrate, but the medusa is free-swimming.

7.  DRAW and LABEL two representatives showing the two body forms.

8.  Are members of this phylum found in water or on land?

    *They are found in water.*

9.  Animals show a distinct symmetry in this phylum. DRAW a line through the center of the oral view of the sea jelly on Figure 10.2 below to show how you could divide the sea jelly into equal pieces. Then DRAW two more lines through the center. These animals exhibit **radial symmetry**.

**Figure 10.2 A sea jelly**

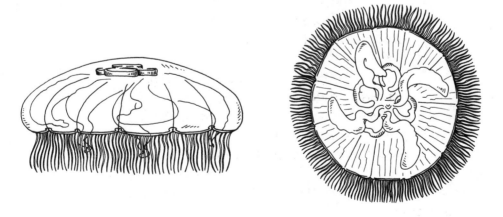

lateral, or side, view                    oral view

STEP 2. Go to the Cnidaria display on the side counter to obtain a depression slide and a *Hydra* sp. specimen. *Hydra* sp. are small freshwater polyps. To get a *Hydra* sp., squeeze the bulb end of the disposable pipette before putting it into the specimen jar. Slowly and carefully release your grip on the bulb to *gently* pull up a *Hydra* sp. Place it on your depression slide and return with it to your lab bench.

STEP 3. Place the slide with the *Hydra* sp. on your compound light microscope and observe. Note the small bumps along the length of the tentacle. These bumps house the **cnidocytes** (stinging cells), which all cnidarians have. Note the small spines coming from the bumps. These spines activate the stinging cells. look @ on low power

STEP 4. Carefully probe one of the tentacles with an edge of an insect pin.

10. Describe the response of your *Hydra*.
the hydra moves slowly to try to eat
It shrivels up

STEP 5. Obtain a water flea from the specimen jar at the Cnidaria display by placing it with a disposable pipette on a depression slide.

STEP 6. Return to your lab bench. Use the disposable pipette to transfer the water flea to the slide with the *Hydra* sp. that is still on the microscope.

11. Describe any feeding reaction that you see.
to it uses its tentacles to grab food

12. Is there any coordinated action between the tentacles? Explain why you think so.   They are independent.

STEP 7. Clean and return the depression slide to the depression slide box at the Cnidaria display.

STEP 8. Obtain a prepared slide of a *Hydra* sp. if necessary for closer observation with your compound light microscope. The *Hydra* sp. has a sac-like digestive system, called a **gastrovascular cavity** lined with cells that produce digestive enzymes.

13. With only one opening to its gastrovascular cavity, how does food waste leave?
the food goes in and out
the same opening

## III. GENERAL CHARACTERISTICS OF THE PHYLUM PLATYHELMINTHES

Members of the animal phylum **Platyhelminthes** demonstrate an increase in complexity with three germ tissue layers and a new kind of body symmetry. Members of this phylum also have organized organ systems and free-living members have a unique **flame cell** to rid the body of metabolic waste. This phylum includes free-living flatworms, tapeworms and flukes.

### Materials

on side counter

Platyhelminthes display including

Platyhelminthes chart and representative classes

*Dugesia* sp. internal structures labeled diagram

*Dugesia* sp. live specimen jar

*Dugesia* sp. live specimens in bowl with light

culture water

disposable pipettes to transfer specimens

specimen jars with samples of tapeworms and flukes

hard-boiled egg yolk

toothpicks

watch glass

dissecting microscope

on your lab bench

prepared slide of the tapeworm, *Taenia* sp. scolex

blunt probe

disposable pipette

compound light microscope

### Procedure

STEP 1. Observe the display showing the diversity of the phylum Platyhelminthes on the side counter. Most flatworms are hermaphrodites, having both male and female sexual structures.

14. What is an advantage of being hermaphroditic?

    *they can reproduce*

15. What is a disadvantage of being hermaphroditic?

    *they devote alot of energy to keep the other alive.*

STEP 2. At the display, look at the diagram of the internal structure of the flatworm, *Dugesia* sp.

    16.   What does its digestive system look like?

*It has a gastro vascular cavity lined with cells*

STEP 3. At the display, observe the setup with the lights over a bowl containing *Dugesia* sp. If they move toward the light, they are photopositive. If they move away from the light, they are photonegative.

    17.   Are these flatworms photopositive or photonegative?

*Photonegative*

    18.   Where are the light sensors located on the flatworm's body to detect the difference between light and dark?

*They are the eye spots - one end*

STEP 4. At the Platyhelminthes display, pour culture water to cover the bottom of a watch glass. Then use the disposable pipette at the display to obtain a flatworm, *Dugesia* sp., for closer observation. To do this, squeeze the transfer pipette bulb before placing it next to the worm. Gently tap the worm. The worm will curl up, making it easier to suction into the end of the pipette for transfer to the watch glass.

STEP 5. Return to your lab bench with your worm in the watch glass.

STEP 6. Observe the movement of *Dugesia* sp. with the dissecting microscope. Use the blunt probe to gently probe the animal.

    19.   Describe the movement of *Dugesia* sp. Can you see any structures that are used in movement?

*Stretches and then contracts, it slithers*

    20.   Does the flatworm show a coordinated response to touch? Does one end of the worm lead? If so, this animal exhibits a head region with sensory concentration, called **cephalization**.

*Yes it heads region is where eye spots are.*

21. Which area of its body shows the strongest response to a probe?

the head

STEP 7. Try feeding the *Dugesia* sp. a bit of hard-boiled egg yolk on a toothpick you can get at the display.

22. Where does the food enter and leave?

they are the same opening    head/face

23. How is the response of the flatworm different from that of the *Hydra*?

the head spasms

24. DRAW a line through the flatworm image in Figure 10.3 below that would make a mirror image of the two parts. This worm exhibits **bilateral symmetry**.

**Figure 10.3 A flatworm**

STEP 8. Return your specimen to the *Dugesia* sp. specimen container at the Platyhelminthes display. Wash and return the watch glass.

STEP 9. At your lab bench, use the microscope to observe the prepared slide of the tapeworm parasite, *Taenia* sp. Tapeworms and flukes are parasites of vertebrates, including humans, so their body plan is focused on obtaining nutrients from their host, and on reproduction.

25. What does this parasite use to attach to its host?

its hooks & suckers

26. A tapeworm can grow up to 10 meters long. How many kilometers is that?

.01 km

## IV. GENERAL CHARACTERISTICS OF THE PHYLUM NEMATODA

The phylum **Nematoda** includes another type of worm, the roundworm. Members of this phylum are found in virtually every conceivable habitat, and so it is a very large and diverse phylum. Among other traits, this phylum exhibits bilateral body symmetry and a coordinated nervous system. In addition, this phylum molts its outer **cuticle** ("skin"). They also have a **complete digestive system**, which is a tube with two openings: a mouth and anus. Many are free living in the soil, while others are parasitic in plants and animals.

**Materials**

on side counter
Nematoda display including
Nematoda chart and representative classes
*Ascaris* sp. internal structures labeled diagram or specimen
*Turbatrix* sp. (vinegar eels) live specimens
plain microscope slides and coverslips
disposable pipettes to transfer specimens
used slide container

on your lab bench
compound light microscope

**Procedure**

STEP 1. Observe the Nematoda display showing the diversity of roundworms on the side counter. The nematodes are commonly called roundworms.

27. Identify a common nematode parasite.

Vinegar eels

STEP 2. Look at the display of the male and female dissected *Ascaris* sp. nematodes, a parasite that lives in the digestive tract of mammals. You can see the body cavity. Note the complete digestive tube and reproductive tubes.

28. What are most of the internal structures used for?

reproduction

Nematodes have longitudinal muscles that run along the length of the animal's body. This restricts the kind of movement a nematode can make. However, they do have fluid surrounding their digestive tract that provides resistance for their muscles to push against.

Vinegar eels are small nematode worms. These animals are sometimes found in vinegar and wine vats. You will make observations of the movement of worms in this phylum using live vinegar eels, *Turbatrix* sp.

STEP 3. Locate the vinegar eels, *Turbatrix* sp., at the display. Prepare a wet mount slide using a disposable pipette to transfer a drop of the vinegar eel culture to a plain microscope slide and adding a coverslip.

STEP 4. Return to your lab bench. Examine the vinegar eel with the compound light microscope under medium to high power.

29. Describe the movement of the vinegar eel.

*S shape movement*

30. What kind of body symmetry does the vinegar eel have?

*bilateral*

31. What kind of digestive system do the vinegar eels have?

*a complete digestive center, mouth, tube, anus*

STEP 5. Dispose of your used slide and coverslip in the used slide container at the Nematoda display.

## V. GENERAL CHARACTERISTICS OF THE PHYLUM MOLLUSCA

One of the largest animal phyla is the phylum **Mollusca**. This phylum is very important in the ocean; bivalves, (e.g. clams), the cephalopods (e.g. squid and octopus), and gastropods (e.g. snails) are all mollusks. Members of the phylum Mollusca have bilateral symmetry, a complete digestive tract, and a centralized nervous system (most). Mollusks have a special tissue, the **mantle**, that in bivalves, chitons, and snails secretes a shell to protect the visceral organs. Members of this phylum include both grazing herbivores eating algae and active carnivorous hunters. They have a **foot** that can be used for locomotion or modified into tentacles for capturing prey, as in the cephalopods.

**Materials**

on side counter

Mollusca display including

Mollusca chart and representative classes
snail model
*Helix* sp. live specimens
flat glass plates
Congo red dyed yeast
toothpicks
cotton swab
vinegar
dissecting microscope

**Procedure**

STEP 1. Observe the display showng the diversity of the phylum Mollusca on the side counter.

32. DRAW and LABEL two different looking mollusks below.

*Helix* sp. is the common garden snail that belongs to the phylum Mollusca. The garden snail was imported from Europe to serve as a food source.

STEP 2. Go over to the large snail model at the Mollusca display. Use the model key to identify parts of the snail and answer the following questions.

33. Find the numbers for the following named structures.

antenna _____ 2, 3 _____
radula _____ 20 _____
stomach _____ 22 _____
salivary gland _____ 23 _____
heart _____ 31-33 _____

34. What sex is this snail? Explain your answer.

Hermaphrodie

35. A snail may weigh up to 40 g. How many mg is that?

40,000

STEP 3. Wash your hands. It is important that you wash your hands before and after touching animals with moist absorbent skins. Materials used to test one animal may harm another, if you have some on your hands. Obtain a live snail from the display area and place it on a glass plate and return to your lab bench. As soon as the snail begins to move, slowly turn the glass plate over and observe the action of the foot.

36. Describe how the snail moves forward. Is there evidence of muscles?

The foot on the snail,

STEP 4. Observe the snail with the dissecting microscope. Turn over the plate and observe the mouth from the underside. The **radula**, a muscular tongue containing rows of teeth, should now be visible. Introduce a small amount of Congo-red stained yeast cells on a toothpick to the glass and observe the feeding response.

37. How does the snail use its tongue?

The snails are rasping.

38. How does the snail use its antennae?

*Sense their surroundings*

STEP 5. Observe the snail's shell.

39. Describe the shell and hypothesize about the selective value of its shape.

*The shell is spiral, because they are born that way to be able to get bigger*

STEP 6. Look for the presences of eyes. They eyes are simple pigments that can distinguish light intensity. Touch them gently with a cotton swab.

40. Where are the eyes located?

*On the antennas*

41. What happens when you touch the eyes?

*They retract*

STEP 7. Put a single drop of vinegar on a cotton swab. Being careful not to touch the snail's head with the swab, move the swab near the snail's head to see if a sense of smell is used.

42. What part of the snail's head reacted without being touched?

*The back of the neck does not react to being touched*

STEP 8. Lightly touch the snail along the length of its body with the vinegar-soaked swab.

43. Where on its body is the snail most sensitive?

*It was most sensitive on the eyes*

STEP 9. Return your snail to the terrarium. Clean, dry, and return the glass plate to the Mollusca display on the side counter.

## VI. GENERAL CHARACTERISTICS OF THE PHYLUM ANNELIDA

The phylum **Annelida** includes segmented worms found both in the ocean and on land. The marine polychaetes of this phylum have a distinguishable head and podia ("feet"). Leeches are also found in this group; medicinal leeches secrete a blood thinner and are useful in tissue or limb reattachment because they keep the blood flowing. Earthworms are terrestrial annelids that are very important in farming because they aerate and compost organic material in the soil.

**Materials**

    on side counter
        Annelida display including
            Annelida chart and representative classes
            earthworm model with internal structures or labeled
            diagram
            *Lumbricus terrestris* (earthworm) live specimens
            glass bowls
            paper towels
            cotton swab
            vinegar
            foil

STEP 1. Observe the display showing the diversity of the phylum Annelida on the side counter.

44. What kind of symmetry do annelids have?

    bilateral

STEP 2. Examine the earthworm model.

45. Find the numbers for the following named structures.

| | |
|---|---|
| metanephridia | 15 |
| cerebral ganglia (brain) | 14 |
| hearts | 11 |
| seminal vesicles | 16 |
| testes | 21 |
| seminal receptacle | 16 |
| ovaries | 17 |

digestive system

| | |
|---|---|
| pharynx | 2 |
| esophagus | 3 |
| crop | 4 |
| gizzard | 5 |
| intestine | 6 |

46. How does the complexity of the digestive systems of annelids compare to that of nematodes?

*they are more complex*

47. Do earthworms have separate sexes?

*no - hermaphrodites*

You will observe the movement and responsive activities of *Lumbricus terrestris*, the common earthworm.

STEP 3. *Wash your hands.* It is important that you wash your hands before and after touching animals with moist absorbent skins. Materials used to test one animal may harm another if you have some remaining on your hands. Place a moist paper towel on the bottom of a bowl and then put a live earthworm on it. Return to your lab bench to observe the worm with the dissecting microscope.

48. The earthworm has small protruding bristles called setae that aid in its locomotion. How are these bristles used?

*to help get through soil.*

STEP 4. Cover part of the bowl with foil to create lighted and darkened areas. If the earthworm moves toward the light, it is photopositive. If it moves away from the light, it is photonegative.

49. Is the earthworm photopositive or photonegative?

*Photonegative.*

STEP 5. Gently turn your earthworm over.

50. How does the earthworm turn itself back to a normal position?

*Scrunches up its segments*

STEP 6. Use a cotton tipped swab with a single drop of vinegar and gently touch the worm's body in several places along its length.

51. Which area of the worm's body is the most sensitive?

*the middle responded right away.*

STEP 7. Return your earthworm to the display bowl. Clean and return all other materials and wash your hands.

**SUMMARY QUESTION**

Describe the use of structures and systems that show how the nervous and muscle tissue works in each animal phylum you studied and how this action is used by the animal to get food. One member of your group may be asked to share this with the class during discussion.

*the muscle tissues showed us how the organisms move and react to food and stimulus.*

**POST-LAB QUESTIONS**                    **Name** _____

1. With respect to obtaining food, how does the movement of bilaterally symmetric animals differ from radially symmetric animals?

2. How does being flat compensate for lack of a circulatory or respiratory system?

3. What is an advantage of having a complete digestive system?

4. How does fluid in an internal body cavity, like you saw in the round worms and the segmented worms, help with movement?

5. Which animal phylum(a) that you studied has(ve) radial symmetry?

6. Which animal phylum(a) that you studied has(ve) complete digestive systems?

7. Identify the animal phylum that matches the description.

    complete digestive system and molts
    filter feeders and spicules for support
    gastrovascular cavity and flame cells
    radula and muscular foot
    segmented with controlled movement
    stinging cells to stun prey

# ANIMALS, PART TWO

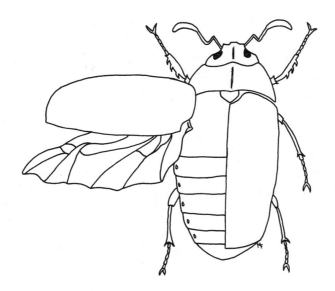

How do developmental similarities help us sort animals into major subgroups? What traits do members of the largest animal phylum have? How do animals balance their need for food with their specific adaptations to live in a particular physical environment? How can experimentation be used to understand and observe animals more closely? These questions will form the framework for your activities in today's lab.

How do developmental similarities help us sort animals into major subgroups? In the last lab we examined two ways the animal phyla are grouped. One was using the criteria of true tissues, and the second was identifying the number of embryonic germ layers. The third way further sorts animal phyla with three embryonic germ tissue layers by observing another developmental process that creates digestive openings. If the first opening is a mouth the animal is a **protostome**. If the mouth forms after an anus the animal is a **deuterostome**. The protostome animal phyla you have studied include the Platyhelminthes, Nematoda, Mollusca, and Annelida. Protostomes are further characterized and sorted by whether they grow by **molting** their outermost skin or shell. Animal phyla that molt include Nematoda, which you examined in the last lab, and Arthropoda, which you will study in today's lab. Today you will also examine two deuterostome phyla, the Echinodermata and Chordata. Please refer also to Appendix G, Classification of Animals.

What traits do members of the largest animal phylum have? Which traits enabled members of the largest animal phylum to colonize so many different habitats in such great numbers? The largest and therefore most successful animal phylum with respect to diversity is Arthropoda. Look for developments that helped them live and acquire food in diverse habitats.

How do animals balance their need for food with their specific adaptations to live in a particular habitat? In this lab you will see how natural selection took the two deuterostome phyla that you will study, Echinodermata and Chordata, in quite different directions in their respective habitats.

How can experimentation be used to understand and observe animals more closely? Biologists can take advantage of the fact that animals move about looking for food and mates, providing us the opportunity to experiment.

**PRE-LAB QUESTIONS**                     Name _____

1.  How are animal phyla grouped together?

2.  What is the largest animal phylum?

**STUDENT LEARNING OUTCOMES**

Upon completion of this lab, you will be able to do the following:

I. describe the general characteristics of the phylum Arthropoda,
II. design and conduct experiments to learn about an animal species,
III. describe the general characteristics of the phylum Echinodermata,
IV. describe the general characteristics of the phylum Chordata, and
V. compare design similarities and differences reflecting adaptations in chordate skeletons among species

## I. THE GENERAL CHARACTERISTICS OF THE PHYLUM ARTHROPODA

The largest phylum, in terms of diversity of species, is Arthropoda. Animals in Arthropoda have protostome development. Well-known members of the phylum include insects, spiders, ticks, mites, shrimp, crab, and lobsters. Members of this phylum are segmented, with jointed appendages that can be specialized into structures for sensing and grasping food, walking, swimming, and communicating. They have excellent senses.

An exoskeleton made of **chitin** serves to protect an animal and provide points of attachment for muscles. Two problems arise because of this covering. One problem is the difficulty in supplying oxygen to the internal tissues. This is solved in two ways. Some arthropods that live on land have small tubules (trachea) located along the abdomen that open to the external environment by means of small pores called spiracles. Arthropods that live in water or moist environments have thin tissues called gills used for gas exchange. The second problem deals with the animal's ability to increase in body size. The amount of space for growth inside an exoskeleton is limited.

1. What has to happen for a young arthropod to grow?

    It has to molt.

**Materials**
on side counter
Arthropoda display including
Arthropoda chart and representative classes
preserved specimens of crab, spider, and grasshopper
specimen display of the life stages of a butterfly
model of honeybee
live ladybug collection

**Procedure**

STEP 1. Go over to the side counter to view the display on Arthropoda diversity. One way that different classes in this phylum can be sorted is by counting the number of their appendages.

2. Identify the number of body appendages found on the following arthropods.

Crab        _____10_____

Spider      _____8_____

Grasshopper _____6_____

3. Do members of this phylum exhibit cephalization? Explain your answer.

Yes it does, The head is visible and able to tell it is ahead

Some arthropods exhibit functional specialization during the different periods of their life cycle. After hatching from **eggs**, some insects will start life as worm-like **larvae**, "eating machines", then **metamorphose** through an interim **pupal** stage into **adult** "sex machines" designed primarily for reproduction. These stage changes occur when there is a change in the **hormones**, chemicals the body produces to regulate internal processes.

STEP 2. Observe the butterfly display, an insect that undergoes a complete metamorphosis.

4. What is the advantage of having multiple life stages?

One stage foouses on one task

The largest class in Arthropoda is the class Hexapoda, the insects. A major contributor to the great success and radiation of insects is their ability to fly.

5. What is an advantage of flight?

get food, lay eggs where predators can not get too.

On the side counter is a large model of a honeybee, *Apis mellifera*. Bees are very important to agriculture, because they are primary pollinators, transferring pollen that contains the male gametes, to the female part of a flower.

STEP 3. Observe the parts of the bee closely. Find the head, thorax, and abdomen, identified as A, B, and C.

6. Where are the legs attached?

thorax

7. Insect wings develop as extensions of the cuticle. How many wings does the honeybee have?

4

8. Find the numbers for the following named structures. Circle those structures used for reproduction.

| | |
|---|---|
| tongue | 3 |
| honey bladder | 10 |
| Malpighian tubules | 19 |
| ovaries | 29 |
| uterine tubes | 30 |
| vagina | 32 |
| venom bladder | 41 |

9. What impact do the larval and adult stages of insects have on the farming industry?

Catapilars eat Crops but butterflies polinate Crops

STEP 4. Spend a few minutes observing the live population of ladybugs, a species of beetle, on display. Ladybugs are in the largest order of insects, order Coleoptera; this order has successfully radiated into over 350,000 species! The outermost set of their wings is leathery, and open up to reveal membranous inner wings used for flight.

10. List five phenotypic or behavioral differences you see among individual ladybugs. Be specific.

# Spots, size, shade of red, move more, Wings stick out.

11. Explain why there are differences among individuals in the population.

*differences among individuals in population*

## II. EXPERIMENTATION WITH LIVE ANIMALS

You will learn about pill bug preferences and behaviors by setting up two experiments. Before your begin, review the steps of the scientific method outlined on page 13.

### Materials

on side counter

live pill bug collection
spoon for transfer of pill bugs
Petri dish
filter paper cut into half circles
water bottle
small square of cardboard
sample foods

### Procedure

STEP 1. On the side counter, carefully observe another arthropod, the pill bug, a crustacean.

12. List three things that make a pill bug different from a ladybug. Provide specific details.

*coils up and doesn't fly*
*pill bugs have gills*

STEP 2. Find the materials for this experiment on the side counter. Place a piece of filter paper inside a Petri dish. Completely moisten the filter paper using the water bottle, being careful not to wet the opposite side of the Petri dish. Use the spoon to add ten pill bugs from the collection to the dry side of the Petri dish, i.e., in the area opposite to the wet paper.

*Please handle the pill bugs carefully so that you do not injure them.*

STEP 3. Place the lid on the Petri dish, then cover the entire Petri dish with cardboard. Take your Petri dish with the pill bugs to your lab bench and note the time. You will wait thirty minutes before removing the cardboard.

13. What hypothesis is being tested?

*Pill bug goes to the moist side*

*At this time, you may proceed with the next activity, and then return to this experiment.*

STEP 4. After 30 minutes remove the cardboard, and observe the location of the pill bugs. *Keep the pill bugs for a second experiment that you will design yourself.*

14. Record your group and class results on Table 11.1 below.

**Table 11.1 Location of pill bugs**

|  | number on the wet side | number on the dry side |
|---|---|---|
| your group | 4 | 1 |
| class average | 4 | 1 |

15. What is the independent variable in this design?

*Moistness of towels*

16. What are you measuring?

*location of pill bugs*

17. Compare your group data to the class data and comment on sample size by considering the following questions. What is your sample size? How does replication of the experiment affect your conclusion?

18. What is your conclusion?

Pill bugs prefer a dark moist enviroment

19. Knowing more about pill bugs, where would you look for them when you are outside?

moist dark enviroment

20. Pill bugs can weigh approximately 157 mg. How many g is that?

STEP 5. Design an experiment to test the eating preferences of pill bugs. On the side counter will find various materials for you to select for your experiment.

21. What is your hypothesis?

22.  Write out the materials and methods of your experimental design here.

STEP 6. Review your hypothesis and experimental design with your instructor before you proceed.

23.  Instructor initials _____

STEP 7. Run your experiment.

24.  Record your results below.

25. Analyze your results and state your conclusion.

26. If you were to run your experiment again, what might you do differently to improve it?

STEP 8. *Carefully return the pill bugs to the original container without injuring them.* Discard the food items and used filter papers into the trash. Clean and return the Petri dish and cardboard to the side counter where you initially found them.

## III. THE GENERAL CHARACTERISTICS OF THE PHYLUM ECHINODERMATA

Echinodermata is one of the two deuterostome phyla you will observe today. This is a relatively small marine phylum with respect to species numbers, but includes important predators of the intertidal zone, the sea stars. Other members of this phylum are brittle stars, sea urchins, sea cucumbers, and sea lilies. Members of this phylum have an endoskeleton made of calcium carbonate (chalk) and a "spiny" skin that can quickly stiffen up when touched. They move by means of **water-vascular** system, a fluid-filled hydraulic system that extends throughout their body. Water enters this system through a sieve plate, the **madreporite. Tube feet**, which are extensions of this system used for locomotion, are hydraulically controlled. Because of its large surface area, the water vascular system also functions in gas exchange. Echinoderms have complete digestive systems and separate sexes that release gametes into the ocean.

**Materials**

on side counter

Echinodermata display including

Echinodermata chart and representative classes

model of sea star, *Asterias* sp.

preserved sea urchin

sea urchin test

demonstration slide of sea urchin larva

**Procedure**

STEP 1. Observe the display of echinoderm diversity.

27. What kind of body symmetry do adult echinoderms have?

*have radical body*

STEP 2. Examine the details of the sea star by looking over the model.

28. Match the structures below by identifying their numbers on the model.

components of the water vascular system:

| madreporite | 7 |
|---|---|
| circular canal | 10 |
| radial canal | 11 |
| ampulla | 13 |
| tube feet | 15 |

some components of digestion:

| stomach | 1/2 |
|---|---|
| hepatic ceca | 3 |
| anus | 5 |

other components:

| nerve ring | 18 |
|---|---|
| radial nerve | 17 |

STEP 3. At the display area, observe the preserved sea urchin specimen and its endoskeleton, called a **test**. The bumps on the test are where the spines attached. The small round disk on the upper surface is the madreporite where water enters the water vascular system.

29. DRAW and LABEL the sea urchin test below, left, and the whole animal below, right.

30. What do you think the holes in the test are for?

STEP 4. Observe the sea urchin larvae at the demonstration microscope.

31. What kind of symmetry do they have? How you think that their perception of their surroundings might change as they transition from larvae to adults?

32. If you see a new organism in a tide pool, what characteristics would you use to identify the animal as an echinoderm?

## IV. THE GENERAL CHARACTERISTICS OF THE PHYLUM CHORDATA

Chordata is the second of the two deuterostome phyla you will observe today. While members in the phylum Echinodermata radiated in the oceans, member of the phylum Chordata spread out in the oceans, on land, and in the air. This is the phylum that includes you! Members of the phylum Chordata share unique embryonic features including a flexible notochord, a dorsal nerve cord, pharyngeal (throat) slits, and a post-anal tail. The phylum Chordata includes all the animals with a backbone to protect the dorsal nerve cord, the vertebrates, as well as some invertebrate classes. Invertebrate chordates include sea squirts and lancelets. Common vertebrates include fish, amphibians (e.g. frogs), reptiles (e.g. lizards and snakes), birds, and mammals. Vertebrate members of this phylum have an **endoskeleton**, an internal skeletal support system. Skeletal muscles move their bony support system. The largest living animal is in this group; it is the blue whale, a mammal. Vertebrates have complex internal organ systems for digestion, excretion, circulation, respiration, and reproduction. Their nervous and endocrine (hormone) systems control all the other systems.

The most diverse vertebrate class includes the ray-finned bony fish. Bony fish have a fantastic ability to extract oxygen from the water through the design of their gills. The largest fish are in another class that includes sharks. Sharks have a skeleton made of the lighter weight support material, cartilage. The most diverse class on land is Aves (birds); flying birds have airy, lightweight bones and feathers. Birds have superior respiratory and circulatory systems. The most intelligent vertebrate class is the mammals, with extensive nervous systems. Both birds and mammals can maintain high levels of activity because they control their internal body temperatures with a high metabolic rate.

### Materials

> on side counter
>> Chordata display including
>>> Chordata chart and representative classes
>>> live frog, *Rana* sp.

### Procedure

STEP 1. Observe the display of chordate diversity on the side counter.

33. What evidence of cephalization do you see?

34. Identify a chordate suited to the water and one suited to life on land. Justify your answer.

The leopard frog, *Rana* sp., is as an example of a vertebrate. It is an amphibian (dual lives) that spends its larval stage completely in water and its adult stage partly in water and partly on dry land.

STEP 2. Move along the side counter until you see the frog in a chamber.

35.   Does the frog have any body symmetry? If so, explain what kind.

36.   Does the frog have some kind of support system? If so, explain what kind you think it is and explain why you think so.

37.   In terms of number of animals, the exoskeleton has been the most successful design. However, for large size, the endoskeleton has been more successful. Do you agree with these statements? Explain why or why not.

STEP 3. Notify you instructor that you are ready to observe the frog in different environments. The instructor will remove a frog from the aquarium and place it in a terrarium.

STEP 4. Observe the movement of the frog on land. The instructor may prod the frog gently with the glass rod.

38.   Describe how the frog moves itself forward.

39.   Explain how the ways the legs are attached affect the frog's locomotion on land.

STEP 5. The leopard frog is semi-aquatic as an adult. The instructor will place the frog into an aquarium that is partly filled with water.

40.  Describe at least three traits in the frog's anatomy that demonstrate its adaptation to water. Explain how those traits help the frog.

## V. DESIGN OF THE SKELETON IN MEMBERS OF CHORDATA

The owl pellet will be your source for small vertebrate bones so that you may compare various vertebrate skeletons. Barn owls eat small mammals and birds. However, they don't have teeth to break bones into smaller pieces. Owls will catch and swallow their small prey whole and the soft digestible parts are separated from the indigestible fur, feathers, and bone in the owl's gizzard. The soft digestible parts pass into the stomach and down their digestive tract. The bones and other indigestible parts are wrapped in the prey's fur or feathers in the gizzard. The owl regurgitates the wrapped bones without damaging their throats.

**Materials**
>      on side counter
>>            owl pellet
>>            sorting plate
>>            forceps
>>            probe
>>            beaker for animal waste
>>            human skeleton
>>            charts of small owl prey skeletons
>
>      on your lab bench
>>            watch glass
>>            dichotomous keys for bones
>>            labeled bone sorting sheet
>>            ruler

**Procedure**
STEP 1. At the side counter, obtain an owl pellet, a sorting plate, forceps and a probe for your lab group.

STEP 2. At your lab bench, unwrap and place the pellet on the larger side of the sorting plate, and gently tease apart the bones from the fur or feathers using the forceps and probe.

STEP 3. Put the separated bones on the smaller side of the sorting plate.

STEP 4. Set up a dissecting microscope for further evaluation of the bones.

STEP 5. Refer to the reference sheet when necessary. Select a jaw bone from your isolated bones and place it on a watch glass for closer observation with the dissecting microscope.

41.  Is there a **diastema** (gap) between the incisors and the cheek teeth?

42.  Are the teeth lobed, angled, or pointed?

STEP 6. Measure the length of the jaw using the ruler.

43.  Record the length of the jaw.

_____ mm

STEP 7. Use the dichotomous key to identify the animal you found and place it on your sorting sheet.

STEP 8. Remove all the other jaw bones in your sample, and identify them by species. Place all bones onto the sorting sheet.

STEP 9. Refer to the "Identifying owl pellet contents" chart or other charts on display. Find a shoulder blade, hip bone, upper leg bone, and lower leg bone from your sample. Compare them to the human skeleton at the front of the room or on the chart.

44.  How are the shoulder blades of the human and the small animal different?

STEP 10. Compare the design of the hip, upper leg, and lower leg bones of the small animal with the human skeleton.

45. What similarities and differences do you see in the construction of the lower leg skeleton?

46. List the different animals you found in the owl pellet. Describe and explain your evidence.

STEP 11. Present your evidence to the instructor for confirmation.

47. Instructor initials _____

STEP 12. Clean up by discarding the hair and/or feathers and bones in the designated beaker on the side counter. Wash and dry the sorting plate. Return all materials including the dichotomous keys and sorting sheets.

**SUMMARY QUESTION**

Describe the traits seen in members of the phylum Arthropoda that enabled that phylum to diversify. Describe the unique traits of the phylum Echinodermata and the phylum Chordata. One member of your group may be asked to share this with the class during discussion.

**POST-LAB QUESTIONS**                    Name _____

1. Identify two traits shared by members of the phyla Echinodermata and Chordata not seen in the other animal phyla you observed.

2. Hypothesize why the skeletons of vertebrates you studied today have the same general bone types.

3. What is an advantage of bilateral body symmetry?

4. How do you distinguish between an animal that is not cephalized from one that is cephalized?

5. The term for molting is **ecdysis**. What are the two animal phyla that need to molt in order to grow larger? How do they use their coverings to their advantage?

6. Under proper conditions, a leopard frog can jump over 10X its body length! Imagine our frog jumped 155 cm. How many meters is that? How many meters could you jump if you could leap like a frog?

7. Complete the checklist on the next page in Table 11.2 of developments in animal phyla.

**Table 11.2 Checklist of traits observed in animal phyla**

| phylum | type of symmetry none (-) radial (R) bilateral (B) | number of germ layers | type of digestive system none (-) gastrovascular cavity (GV) complete (C) | locomotion (list structures) | cephalization absent (-) present (+) | segmentation absent (-) present (+) |
|---|---|---|---|---|---|---|
| Porifera | | | | | | |
| Cnidaria | | | | | | |
| Platyhelminthes | | | | | | |
| Nematoda | | | | | | |
| Mollusca | | | | | | |
| Annelida | | | | | | |
| Arthropoda | | | | | | |
| Echinodermata | | | | | | |
| Chordata | | | | | | |

# ANIMALS, PART THREE

How are complex animals organized? What terms of direction are used when studying the anatomy of an animal? What are the major organ systems? How does the environment shape the body plan of an animal? These questions will form the framework for your activities in today's lab.

How are complex animals organized? Animals are organized in a hierarchical manner. The smallest unit of an organism that has the properties of life is the cell. Collections of cells working together to perform a function are called tissues. The major tissue types in animals are muscle, nervous, **connective**, and **epithelial**. Muscle and nervous tissues respond to stimuli; you saw that response in "Animals", parts one and two. Connective tissue such as bone, blood, fat, tendons and ligaments is the most abundant tissue, and makes up structures that support and connect the other tissues. Epithelial tissue is the special tissue that interfaces with whatever is outside the organism; for example, it makes up the upper surface of the skin. Multiple tissue types are used to make an **organ** that performs a particular function. Examples of organs are the heart, stomach, and lung. Organs that work together make an **organ system**. For example, the cardiovascular system includes the heart, blood vessels, and blood that work together to transport materials throughout the body. Animals have multiple organ systems that specialize in their function, with the goal of maintaining homeostasis. You will be investigating the hierarchy of the **digestive system** in this lab.

What terms of direction are used when studying the anatomy of an animal? Anatomy is the study of the structures of an organism. With animals, it is useful to investigate them externally and then internally. Externally, if an animal has bilateral symmetry, then they have an **anterior** end where cephalization occurs. The opposite end of the animal is the **posterior**. The belly side of an animal is its **ventral** surface, and the upper side is called the **dorsal** surface.

How does the environment shape the body plan of an animal? The external shape of an animal species that best suits its environment will be naturally selected over time. For example, the overall shape may become streamlined to reduce friction as seen in fish, dolphins, and penguins. Natural selection has worked to ensure that the most suitable structures survive. Cephalization increased as an adaptation to improve response toward food. As cephalization increased, the brain and sensory organs were encased for protection in a skull. Two distinctly different habitats providing different challenges are the water and the land. In today's lab, you will be comparing selected adaptations of an aquatic animal and a terrestrial animal.

*Gloves for examination and dissection are required. Please bring a package of gloves.*

**PRE-LAB QUESTIONS**                    **Name** _____

1.  What is a tissue?

2.  What are the major tissue types found in an animal?

3.  Provide an example of an organ system and its function.

4.  Think of an animal that lives in the water and one that lives on land. How do their external structures differ?

5.  What advantage does cephalization give an animal?

*PLEASE NOTE: A package of gloves for examination and dissection is required for this lab. Please bring a package of gloves.*

*A package of gloves for examination and dissection is required for this lab.*

**STUDENT LEARNING OUTCOMES**

Upon completion of today's lab, you will be able to do the following:

  I. identify the anatomical terms of direction, and the external structures of a crayfish and a rat,
  II. identify the locations and functions of the major organs of a crayfish and a rat,
  III. describe the hierarchical organization of an animal, and
  IV. compare adaptations in body plan to habitat.

## I. ANATOMICAL TERMS OF DIRECTION AND EXTERNAL ANATOMY

It is useful to refer to common anatomical terms of direction when examining an animal. In the rat below, you can see that the belly side is **ventral**, the spine side is **dorsal**. The nose is at the **anterior** end and at the **posterior** is the tail. See Figure 12.1 below.

**Figure 12.1 The rat with anatomical terms of direction**

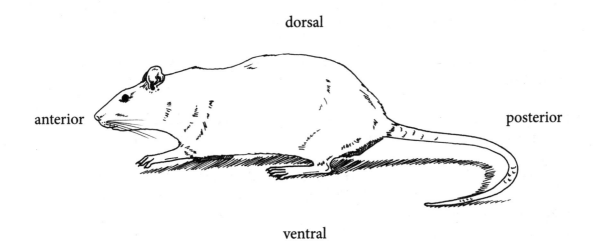

### I. A. The external anatomy of the crayfish

There are numerous species of crayfish worldwide living in freshwater ponds or rivers. Crayfish are most active at night, i.e. **nocturnal**. They eat snails, algae, insect larvae, worms, tadpoles, and fish eggs and are eaten by fish such as trout and bass, and by us!

**Materials**

> on side counter
>> male and female crayfish
>> dissecting tray
>> dissecting utensils (forceps, probes, scissors, scalpels)
>> dissecting microscope
>
> on your lab bench
>> dissection guide of crayfish
>> magnifying glass
>> watch glass

**Procedure**

STEP 1. Put on gloves for examination.

STEP 2. You will work in pairs for the examinations of this lab. Coordinate with the other students at your lab bench so that both sexes will be examined at each bench. Decide which team will obtain the male and which team will obtain the female.

STEP 3. One student from each team will collect a preserved crayfish from the side counter by placing it in a dissecting tray and return with it to your lab bench. *You will be using the same crayfish for multiple activities, so please do not discard the crayfish until indicated.*

STEP 4. One student from each team will collect dissecting utensils from the side counter for your use.

STEP 5. Study Figure 12.1 on the previous page so that you can identify the dorsal, ventral, anterior, and posterior of the animal. Place the animal ventral side down on the tray.

The exoskeleton of the crayfish, the **carapace**, covers the body of the crayfish. The animal is divided into major regions: the head, thorax, and abdomen. The head and thorax together are known as the **cephalothorax**.

1. What kind of symmetry does the crayfish exhibit?

   bilateral

2. Suggest two possible functions of the carapace.

   Protection , Structure

3. What is the main difference in the carapace between the cephalothorax and the abdomen?

*Carapace - the tail has sections - segments*

*cephalothorax - one big section*

4. Given the traits you see in the crayfish, and using your experience from the two previous labs, what phylum includes crayfish?

*octopus*

**Figure 12.2 The external anatomy of the crayfish**

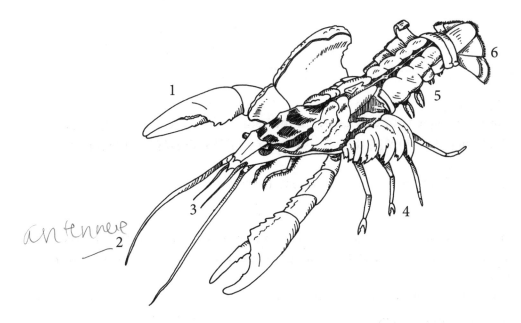

*antennae*

STEP 6. Compare the crayfish in Figure 12.2 above with your crayfish and the crayfish dissection guide at your lab bench.

5. Identify the following structures by the number on Figure 12.2:

      antennae    - 2
      antennules  - 3
      chelipeds   - 1
      swimmerets  - 5
      tail        - 6
      walking legs - 4

6. Which appendages are used to grab prey?

Cheliped s

7. In what specific ways does the crayfish demonstrate cephalization?

it has a head, antenna, eyes

STEP 7. Turn your crayfish over to observe the ventral surface of your animal. The last abdominal segment forms a **tail** fan.

8. How many pairs of walking legs do you see?

4 pairs

9. Closely examine your crayfish from the ventral side. Use the magnifying glass if you wish. How many pairs of swimmerets does the crayfish have?

5 pairs

STEP 8. In male crayfish the two most anterior pairs of swimmerets are enlarged and hardened. Compare your specimen to another group's so that you can identify both sexes.

10. Is your specimen a male or female?

female

11. After looking at these appendages, and thinking about how it can move, propose a location in the water where you might find crayfish.

the river by rocks - Shallow water

STEP 9. Use the forceps to lift the surface of one of the eyes and snip with scissors to remove it. Place the eye on a watch glass for observation with the dissecting microscope. *Remove your gloves and wash your hands before using the dissecting microscope.*

12.  Describe the surface texture of the eye.

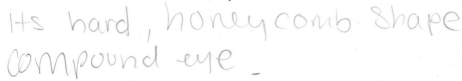
Its hard, honeycomb shape compound eye

STEP 10. *Save the crayfish specimen for further study.*

## I. B. The external anatomy of the rat

**Materials**
>   on side counter
>       male and female rats
>       dissecting tray

**Procedure**
STEP 1. Put on gloves for examination.

STEP 2. Coordinate with the other students at your lab bench so that both sexes will be examined at each bench. Decide which team will obtain the male and which team will obtain the female.

STEP 3. One student from each team will collect a preserved rat from the side counter by placing it in a dissecting tray and return with it to your lab bench. *You will be using the same rat for multiple activities, so please do not discard the rat until indicated.*

STEP 4. Refer back to Figure 12.1 and identify the dorsal, ventral, anterior, and posterior of the animal. Place the animal ventral side down on the tray.

13.  What kind of symmetry does the rat exhibit?

bilateral

STEP 5. Observe the external surface of the rat.

14.  Does the rat have an exoskeleton like the crayfish? Is there any evidence of a support system in this animal?

endo

The skin of the rat is soft and covered with fur.

15.  Suggest a possible function of the fur.

*Warmth, protection*

16.  In what specific ways does the rat demonstrate cephalization?

*mouth, nose, eyes*

STEP 6. Look closely at the appendages and tail of the rat.

17.  What structures are used to grip the surface of its environment?

*Claws*

18.  Suggest how the rat moves and uses its tail.

*walk, climb, run, swim, tail for balance*

19.  Given the traits you see in the rat, and using your experience from the two previous labs, what phylum includes rats?

*Cordaca*

STEP 7. *Save the rat specimen for further study.*

## II. INTERNAL ANATOMY AND MAJOR ORGANS

Animals are heterotrophic. To get the most energy from their food, animals use aerobic respiration. **Respiratory** systems developed for gas exchange in order to bring in oxygen and release carbon dioxide. A **cardiovascular** system with a heart and blood vessels improved the efficiency of movement of nutrients and gases. **Nervous** system improvements included development of special senses for detecting prey. Separate sexes for reproduction improved the genetic variability of a species. The digestive system became partitioned into functional organs to improve the mechanical and chemical breakdown of food and the absorption of nutrients.

### II. A. The internal anatomy of major organ systems in the crayfish

**Materials**

    on side counter

        dissecting pins

        magnifying glass

        dissecting utensils (forceps, probes, scissors, scalpels)

        blunt metal probe

        model of crayfish

    on your lab bench

        crayfish in dissecting tray

        crayfish dissection guide

**Procedure**

STEP 1. Return to your crayfish specimen.

STEP 2. Put on gloves for dissection. Place the crayfish specimen so that ventral side is down on your dissecting tray. Refer to Figure 12.3 on the next page for directions for cutting open the carapace. Follow the cutting sequence on the figure.

**Figure 12.3 External anatomy and cutting directions for the crayfish**

1. Examine your specimen. You will only cut the carapace (exoskeleton).

2. Place scissors under the carapace between the cephalothorax and abdomen.

3. Point scissors upward to avoid cutting internal structures, then cut along the middle of the cephalothorax ending between the eyes.

4. Make a small cut across just below the eyes.

5. Cut the carapace down the middle of the abdomen to the tail.

6. Make small cuts across the carapace of the abdomen at the posterior end.

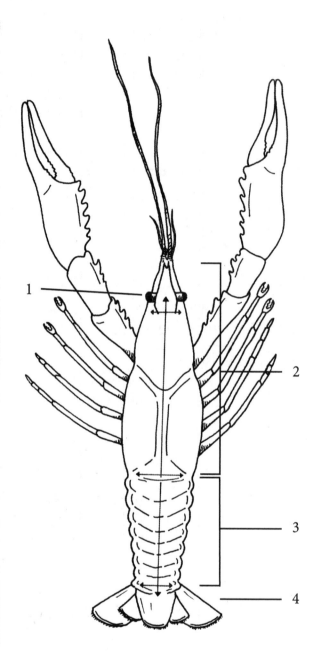

(1) eye            (3) abdomen
(2) cephalothorax  (4) tail

**Figure 12.4 The internal structures of the crayfish**

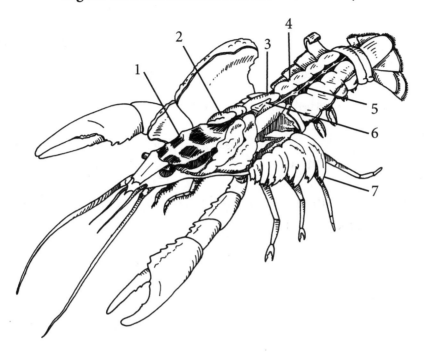

(1) stomach
(2) digestive gland
(3) gonad
(4) abdominal flexor muscle

(5) dorsal abdominal artery
(6) heart
(7) gills

As you proceed with the dissection, refer to Figure 12.4 above and to the model of the crayfish on the side counter.

Begin your exploration with the circulatory system.

STEP 3. Gently move the gills aside with the probe and locate the **heart** (6) and **dorsal abdominal artery** (5). Arteries carry blood away from the heart.

20.  Which major body segment of the crayfish contains the heart?

The thorax

21.  Where does the dorsal abdominal artery take the blood?

by the tail, away from the body    The abdomen & tail.

Continue your exploration with the reproductive system.

STEP 4. Locate the **gonad** (3) that is located deep (more ventral) and posterior to the heart.

22. Knowing the sex of your crayfish, what is the name of the gonad in your specimen?

*Ovaries*

Continue your exploration with the digestive system.

STEP 5. Refer to the diagram and crayfish dissection guide to identify the **mouth, stomach** (1), **digestive gland** (2), and **intestine**.

23. Where is the mouth located? Does this provide evidence for where the crayfish finds food?

*Ventril, food on the botton*

24. Where is the stomach located with respect to the heart?

*the center, the heart is below*
*above the heart*

25. Given the function of the intestine, do you think it wise or unwise to "de-vein" a shrimp, crayfish, or lobster before eating it? Explain why you think so.

*breakdown food - digestion occurs*
*devein to take out intestine,*

Continue your exploration with the nervous system.

STEP 6. Carefully retract the visceral organs (stomach, digestive glands, gonads) with a gloved hand or by using the blunt probe to expose the thread-like whitish nerve cords on the ventral surface.

26. What other parts of a nervous system can you identify?

*eyes, brain, antennas*

Continue your exploration with the muscular system.

STEP 7. Find the large **abdominal flexor muscle** (4).

27.  Muscles contract when working. Which direction will the crayfish move when the large abdominal flexor muscles contract?

*back wards*

28.  Given the size and strength of the muscle, suggest a circumstance when the crayfish might use this muscle over its walking legs.

*get away from predators*

Continue your exploration with the respiratory system.

STEP 8. With the forceps, carefully remove the piece of carapace that you have cut to expose the **gills** (7). Gills are used to extract oxygen from the water, and to release carbon dioxide. It may be necessary to reach underneath with the blunt probe to detach any tissue from the interior of the animal that is attached to the carapace. Using a blunt probe, carefully separate the first row of gills and notice that there is another row underneath. Remove one of the legs and observe how the gills are attached to the walking legs.

STEP 9. Place a small sliver of gill on a watch glass for observation with the dissecting microscope. *Remove your gloves and wash your hands before using the dissecting microscope.*

29.  What is the name of the organ system that includes the gills?

*respitory*

30.  Why are the gills so thin and feathery?

*surface area*

31.  Why are the gills attached to the walking legs?

*to push water*

STEP 10. *Save the crayfish specimen for further study.*

**Figure 12.5 Cutting directions for the rat**

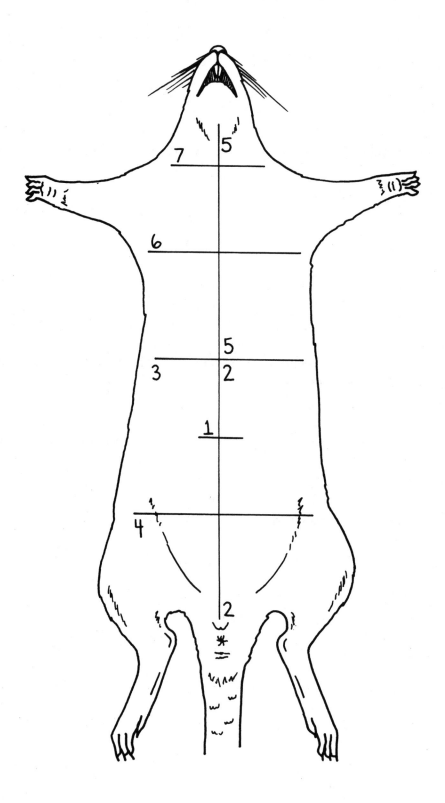

**II. B. The internal anatomy of major organ systems in the rat**

**Materials**
    on side counter
        dissecting pins
        dissecting utensils (forceps, probes, scissors, scalpels)
        string
        blunt metal probe

    on your lab bench
        rat in dissecting tray
        rat dissection guide
        magnifying glass

**Procedure**
STEP 1. Put on gloves for dissection. Place the rat specimen so that ventral side is up on your dissecting tray.

STEP 2. If you have not already done so, collect dissecting utensils and two lengths of string approximately 30 cm each from the side counter.

STEP 3. Refer to Figure 12.5 on the previous page and follow the cutting lines in the order indicated. Cut through just the skin and associated superficial muscles. *Keep the scissors facing upwards to reduce the risk of damaging important internal structures.* Note that the lateral cut lines (cut 3) at the lower end of the rib cage should be made to carefully cut the **diaphragm** (Figure 12.6, number 4, on the next page). The diaphragm is a thin muscle that separates the abdominal cavity from the **thoracic cavity** (chest). Use the scissors to cut the diaphragm close to the exterior wall so that it will separate and fall over the other visceral organs. Once you cut the diaphragm, open the chest cavity by lifting and cutting through the **sternum**. When all your cuts are completed, carry your specimen in the dissecting tray over to the sink and discard excess fluid. Return to your lab bench.

STEP 4. With the rat sill placed ventral-side up on your dissecting tray, tie a piece of string about 30 cm long around the front right foot and wrap the string under the dissecting tray and tie the other end around the front left foot to hold the animal open for further examination. Tie string in a similar fashion around the hind feet. Use dissecting pins to hold open the animal skin as needed.

    32.  How many mm is 30 cm?

**Figure 12.6 The internal anatomy of the rat
heart, respiratory system, and spleen**

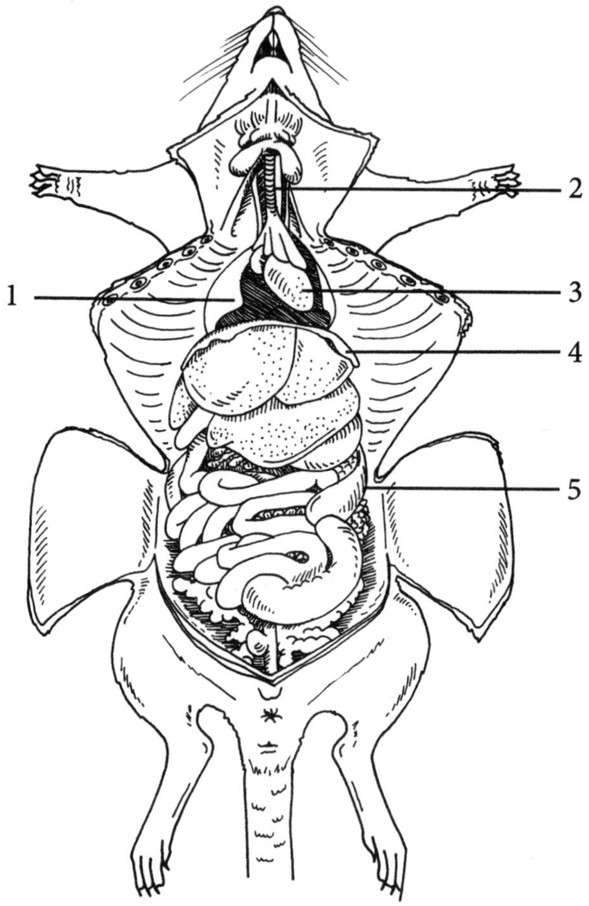

(1) lung          (4) diaphragm
(2) trachea       (5) spleen
(3) heart

Begin your exploration with the respiratory system. Refer to Figure 12.6 above.

STEP 5. Locate the nostrils and oral cavity for ventilation.

33. Suggest two uses of the nose.

Smell and breathing

STEP 6. Use the blunt probe to separate muscle and other tissue in the neck area to expose the **trachea** (2). The trachea is lined with cartilaginous rings and carries air from the oral cavity down to the **lungs** (1).

34.  Propose a reason for the rings around the trachea.

*TO keep it open*

STEP 7. Observe the flat muscle which is the **diaphragm** (4).

The diaphragm contracts and flattens to enlarge the chest cavity.

35.  What direction does air flow when the chest cavity expands?

*air flown In.*

STEP 8. Observe the lungs found in the thoracic cavity. The lungs will inflate when the rat breathes. Each lung has many small air sacs surrounded by tiny blood vessels called **capillaries**.

36.  What process moves oxygen from the lungs into the blood?

*diffusion.    One    Cell Thick*

Continue your exploration with the circulatory system. Refer to Figure 12.6 on the previous page.

STEP 9. Locate the **heart** (3) and major vessels attached to the heart. The largest vessel leaving the heart is the **aorta**. Trace the aorta internally down the dorsal side of the rat. The **spleen** (5) is part of the immune system. The spleen filters, stores, and recycles blood.

37.  Why does the rat need so many large blood vessels?

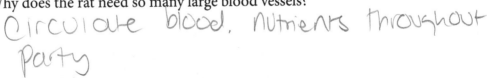

*Circulate blood, nutrients throughout Party*

Continue your exploration with the nervous system.

STEP 10. Note the head of the rat that houses the brain. Protected by the vertebral column is its spinal cord.

38.  Which side of the rat contains the major nerve cord, the spinal cord?

*dorsal*

Continue your exploration with the reproductive system.

STEP 11.  Refer to the rat dissection guide. Record the correct number of the reproductive structures listed to the left of Figures 12.7 and 12.8. Look at specimens of both sexes, which should be at your lab bench.

**Figure 12.7 The male rat**

scrotum         _____

testis          _____

epididymis      _____

vas deferens    _____

seminal
  vescicles     _____

prostate
  gland         _____

penis           _____

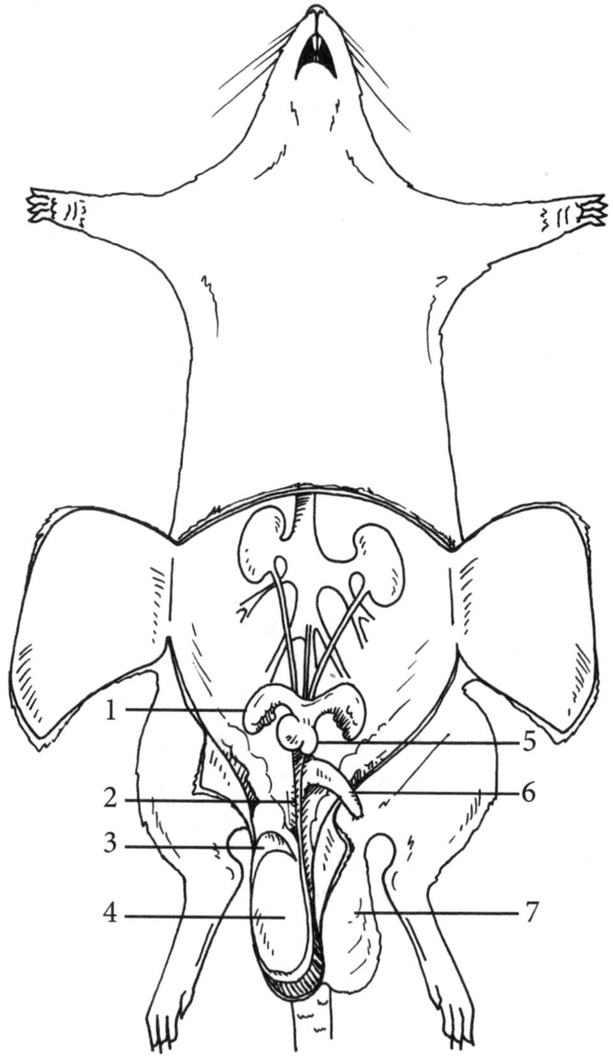

**Figure 12.8 The female rat**

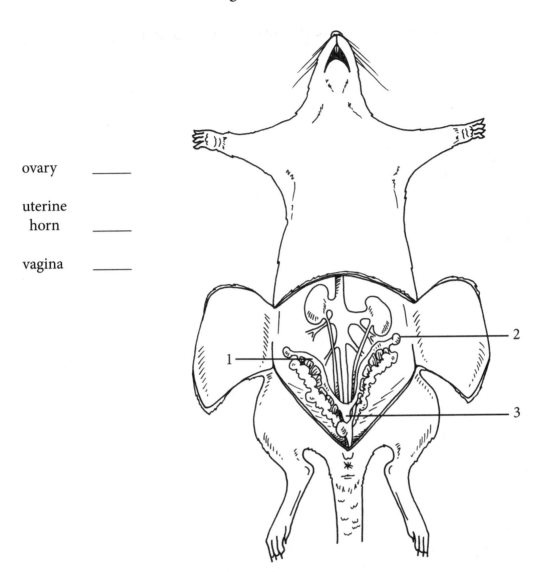

ovary        _____

uterine
  horn       _____

vagina      _____

STEP 12. *Save the rat specimen for further study.*

## III. THE HIERARCHY WITHIN AN ANIMAL

Review the introduction to this lab on page 278. Through your dissections you have seen the complexity of structures found in the crayfish and the rat. Each of these animals has component organ systems that coordinate major bodily functions. The organ systems themselves may have multiple organs that partition up the activities of the system. Those organs are made of different tissues. Tissues are made up of cells, the smallest unit of life. Cells found in different tissues have different appearances in order to perform their specific functions. In this activity you will explore the digestive system organs and tissues.

## ORGANIZATION OF THE DIGESTIVE SYSTEM

Food supplies the body with raw materials for building and repairing tissues, and also is a source of energy. The function of the digestive system is to convert food into useable components. Digestion includes the mechanical and chemical processes to break down foods into macromolecules (such as amino acids, fats, nucleic acids, and simple carbohydrates) and then absorb the molecules. The mammalian digestive system has two large components. First is the **digestive tract**, a tube that food enters into and passes through, and the second component includes the accessory structures that aid in the digestive processes. Controlling the movement from one region of the digestive tract to the next are muscular rings called sphincters.

**Materials**

on side counter
> dissecting pins
> dissecting utensils (forceps, probes, scissors, scalpels)
> string
> blunt metal probe
> prepared slide of small intestine

on your lab bench
> rat in dissecting tray
> dissection guide of rat
> magnifying glass
> watch glass

**Procedure**

STEP 1. Put on gloves for dissection. Continue your observations by tracing the path of food digestion through the digestive tract of the rat. Digestion starts in the **oral cavity** (1) with mechanical breakdown of food, and the addition of moisture and enzymes from the salivary glands. Food moves from the oral cavity through the organs that are sections of the digestive tract, starting with the **esophagus** (2) and then the **stomach (6)**. Open the oral cavity by cutting with scissors posteriorly from the corners of the mouth into the joints of the jaws.

Refer to your specimen and Figure 12.9 on the next page to answer the following questions.

39. What structures are located in the oral cavity? Explain how they help with the digestion of food.

    *Mouth, teeth, tounge, salivary glands*

40. What is the location of the esophagus with respect to the trachea?

    *behind the trachea*

STEP 2. The **stomach** (6) is a muscular organ that produces enzymes and acid to digest proteins. Remove the stomach and cut it open with the scalpel.

41. Propose a reason for the large folds in the stomach.

to expand

Figure 12.9 The digestive system of the rat

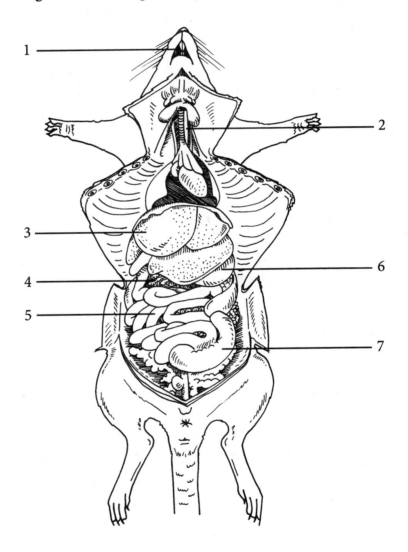

(1) oral cavity
(2) esophagus
(3) liver
(4) pancreas

(5) small intestine
(6) stomach
(7) cecum

Refer to Figure 12.9 on the previous page. Food continues through the tube of the digestive tract by moving from the stomach to the **small intestine** (5). Food moves through the tube by the contraction of smooth muscles that are part of the digestive tract (number 4 of Figure 12.10 on the next page). Organs accessory to the digestive tract also coordinate with digestion in this system. More enzymes are provided by the **pancreas** (4) and small intestine to complete the chemical digestion of foods. The **liver** (3) produces bile that emulsifies fats. Once food is completely broken down into macromolecules, it is absorbed in the small intestine. The next part of the digestive tract is the large intestine. The **large intestine** starts at a blind sac, the **cecum** (7), where microorganisms help animals digest plant material. The large intestine reabsorbs water from all the fluids released into the digestive tract during digestive processing.

STEP 3.  Refer to Figure 12.10 for STEPS 3-6. Use your gloved hands to spread apart the small intestine and the connecting membrane, the **mesentery** (5).

42.  Explain why there are so many blood vessels in the mesentery.

to get blood to intestines for digestion

STEP 4. Follow the small intestine down to the large intestine.

43.  If nutrients are absorbed by the small intestine, what do you propose is the function of the large intestine?

water absorption

STEP 5. Use the scissors to remove a 1 to 2 cm section of the small intestine. Cut it lengthwise and place it open and flat on a watch glass for observation with the dissecting microscope. Small folds (2) along the **lumen** (inside of tube) look like velvet. *Remove your gloves and wash your hands before using the dissecting microscope.*

44.  How many meters is 2 cm?

45.  Suggest why the small intestine is so long and has internal folds that you can observe under the dissecting microscope.

increase surface area

**Figure 12.10 A section of the small intestine, with detail**

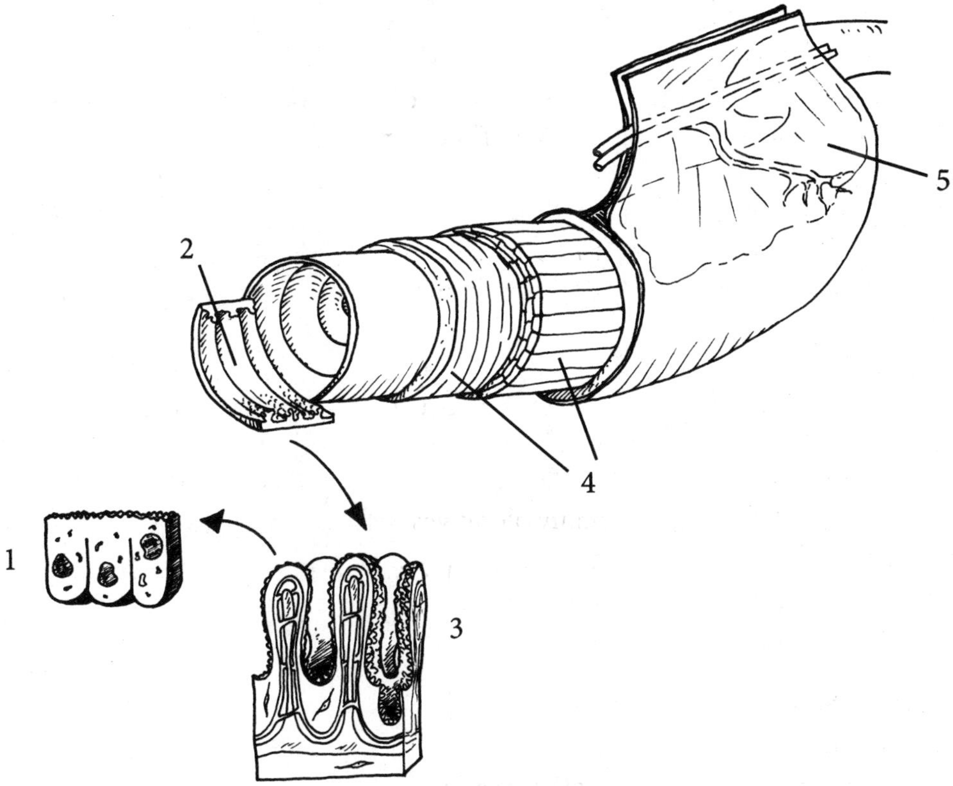

1 = epithelial lining  2 = folds along lumen  3 = villi  4 = muscle layers  5 = mesentery

STEP 6. Get a prepared slide of the small intestine from the side counter to observe with high power on the compound light microscope. You will be able to see the tissues of the **villi** (3)and the surface cells making up the **epithelial lining** (1).

    46.  Describe the microscopic anatomy of the small intestine.

STEP 7. *Save the rat specimen for further study.*

## IV. COMPARISON OF BODY PLAN ADAPTATIONS

**Prcedure.**
STEP 1. Put both the crayfish and rat specimens in front of you for comparison.

STEP 2. Complete Table 12.1 on the next page, comparing the external and internal structures of the crayfish and the rat.

**Table 12.1 Comparison of the crayfish and the rat**

| | crayfish | rat |
|---|---|---|
| habitat | aquatic | land |
| support system | exposkelton | endoskelton |
| location of major muscles for movement | abdomen | legs |
| type of movement(s) possible | walking swimming | walking running |
| organ for gas exchange | Gills | lungs |
| heart location (dorsal, ventral) | dorsal | ventral |
| major nerve location (dorsal, ventral) | ventral | ventral |
| digestive system organs | stomach, esphogus intestine. mouth | stomach, mouth, intestine |
| reproductive system organs | testes ovaries | yes - similar |

47. Of the systems studied in the crayfish, which is most structurally similar to the related rat system? Explain your answer.

similar - skeleton & Heart Of location

48. Of the systems studied in the crayfish, which one is most structurally unlike the related rat system? What is the reason behind these differences?

STEP 3. Put on gloves for cleanup. Separate all the dissection utensils to wash in soapy water, rinse, *dry*, and return to the original position on the side counter. Throw out the preserved animal specimens in the animal waste receptacle on the side counter. Wash the dissection try in soapy water, rinse, *dry*, and return to the original position on the side counter. Remove your gloves, wash your hands, and return the dissecting and compound light microscopes to their respective cabinets. Wipe down your lab bench with cleaner.

**SUMMARY QUESTION**

Identify the components of each organ system studied today and discuss how they are utilized by the rat and crayfish to obtain and process food. One member of your group may be asked to share this with the class during discussion.

**POST-LAB QUESTIONS**          **Name** _____

1.  Both rats and crayfish have legs for walking. Why are the legs of the crayfish relatively smaller?

2.  Order the following in order of increasing size.

    _____ cell
    _____ organ
    _____ organ system
    _____ organism
    _____ tissue

3.  What traits are seen in the rat that places it in its phylum?

4.  What traits are seen in the crayfish that place it in its phylum?

5.  What characteristic is similar between the gills of crayfish and the small intestine of the rat? Explain why.

# PLANTS

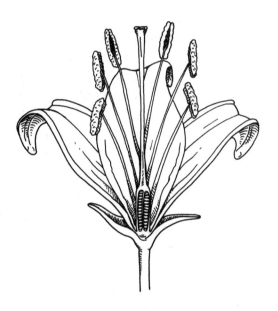

What does a plant use for photosynthesis? What obstacles do plants have to overcome for survival on the land? What are the relationships that exist between plants and organisms of other kingdoms? These questions will form the framework for your activities in today's lab.

What does a plant use for photosynthesis? Plants use carbon dioxide, sunlight, and water for photosynthesis. Plants are eukaryotic **producers** because by photosynthesis they make food for themselves and others in the ecosystem.

What obstacles do plants have to overcome for survival on the land? Limited water and gravity were serious challenges. Millions of years of natural selection resulted in four major morphological developments in plants that allowed them to overcome the challenges of life on land. In early land plants, the first development is found in **bryophytes**, which include mosses. In these plants the gametes are produced in a protected structure called **gametangia**. The second development, seen in plants known as **tracheophytes**, was the evolution of a tube system to transport fluids throughout their bodies. This **vascular tissue** was an important adaptation for life on land for now water and food could easily be transported throughout the plant. This development enabled plants to become very large. The earliest tracheophytes include ferns, and like the bryophytes, ferns produce gametes in gametangia and have flagellated sperm. Their sperm must swim through water to reach an egg. The third big development in plants overcame this limitation. **Seed** plants disperse sperm encased in a coated structure called **pollen**. Wind or animals transfer pollen (with the sperm) to the female part of the plant that produces the egg; water is no longer required for sexual reproduction. The eggs of the seed plants are produced inside **ovules**. Once the egg is fertilized, the ovule is called a seed. The seed is much more than just a zygote. The seed includes the developing embryo, a parental food source, and a protective coat derived from the other structures of the ovule. Seed plants are grouped into phyla that share common traits, the **gymnosperms** and the **angiosperms**. Gymnosperms produce their seeds on specially modified leaves. An example of a gymnosperm is a pine tree that produces seeds on cones. Angiosperms produce seeds in the last of the four major developments in land plants, flowers. The **flower** produces both pollen and ovules. See Appendix G for the classification of major plant phyla.

What are the relationships that exist between plants and organisms of other kingdoms? A major advantage to angiosperms is that the petals of flowers are frequently designed to attract pollinators by color and/or scent. The female component of the flower produces the ovules inside an **ovary**. When the egg in the ovule is fertilized to become a seed, the ovary becomes a **fruit**. Fruits that attract animals and thereby aid in the dispersion of seeds have also been naturally selected. Most vascular plants also have fungi growing around their roots to help absorb water and minerals. Some angiosperms encase special bacteria that fix the element nitrogen into a usable form for them.

**PRE-LAB QUESTIONS**                    **Name** _____

1.  What do plants need for photosynthesis?

2.  What modern plants were the first land plants like?

3.  How does vascular tissue help a plant?

4.  What is the difference between a gamete and a seed?

**STUDENT LEARNING OUTCOMES**

Upon completion of this lab, you will be able to do the following:

      I. state the key developments in plant evolution, and
      II. describe the form and adaptations of plants

## I. PLANT DIVERSITY AND EVOLUTION

In this activity you will observe representatives from the major groups of land plants, and answer questions. Plants follow a basic life cycle that is different from animals. Learning the general cycle will help you understand the structures you will see in the different plant representatives today. As you observe the different plant groups, consider the similarities and differences of the analogous structures such as gametophyte, sporophyte, gametangia, etc. listed in the diagram of the diverse plant phyla.

Plants go through what is called an **alternation of generation**. There are two multicellular forms during the life cycle. The main plant that you see is either a gametophyte or a sporophyte. **Phyte** means "plant-" or "plant-like." The prefix explains what that form of the plant is doing: producing gametes or **spores**. A plant spore is a unicellular haploid cell that can divide to become a multicellular form. Gametes are produced in specialized structures called **gametangia**, and spores are made in **sporangia**. Look at Figure 13.1 below and follow the cycle around. Have you noticed something unusual about plants? Yes, that's it. Plants produce gametes by mitosis!

### Figure 13.1 The life cycle of a plant

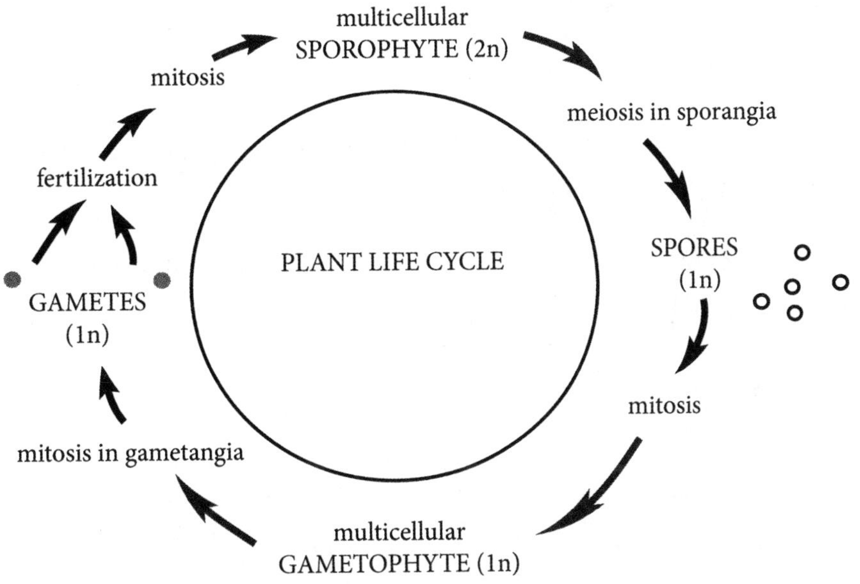

Early photosynthetic life began in the water, and the tiny photosynthetic algae floated on the surface to capture the sunlight. Plants colonized land about 500 million years ago. Moving onto land presented benefits as well as challenges. Carbon dioxide and light are more abundant on land.

## I. A. Bryophytes/ seedless non-vascular plants (mosses and their relatives)

The ancestors to the bryophytes were green algae. Green algae reproduce by releasing motile sperm into water, and the sperm swims to the eggs. Structures evolved in land plants to protect the important gamete-producing tissues. These structures, known as jacketed **gametangia,** are found in all land plants. However, although the gametangia protect the gametes during development, sperm still must swim through water to reach an egg. This still restricts the first land plants, bryophytes, to moist habitats. Because they lack vascular tissue, all necessary materials such as water and minerals, must diffuse from one cell to another. This is a slow process and as a result, bryophytes cannot grow very tall and therefore, are ground-hugging plants.

## Materials
on side counter
chart of moss life cycle
chart of bryophytes
moss specimen
liverwort specimen
demonstration microscope with prepared slide of moss capsule
(sporangium)

on your lab bench
prepared slide of moss archegonium
prepared slide of moss antheridium
compound light microscope

## Procedure
STEP 1. Visit the side counter to observe the live specimens and charts of the non-vascular plants, and answer the following questions.

1. Identify the common names of the non-vascular plants on display.

*Moss, bryophytes liver worst, horn wort*

2. What is the general size and height of the non-vascular plants?

*Small, low to the ground.*

STEP 2. Also at the side counter, observe the slide of the moss capsule, i.e., the moss sporangium.

3. What is inside the moss sporangium? Which plant generation do the spores become? *Spores, sporophyte grows in the gametophite.* *gametophyte*

Plants have two kinds of gametangia. The **archegonium** is the gametangium where eggs are produced. The **antheridium** is the gametangium where sperm are produced. The gametophyte is the dominant multicellular generation in non-vascular plants. The sperm of non-vascular plants swim to the archegonia, and so are dependent on water for sexual reproduction.

STEP 3. Set up and use your compound light microscope to observe the prepared slides of the moss archegonia and antheridia. You will be using the compound light microscope periodically during the lab.

4. Describe any similarity of structure between the two gametangia.

*Protective covering*

5. Identify two reasons why non-vascular plants are found in relatively moist habitats.

*reproduction and easy transport for tissues*

## I. B. Tracheophytes/ seedless vascular plants (ferns and their relatives)

The tracheophytes are the vascular plants. Early plants with this feature include ferns. Some fern relatives grew over a hundred feet tall. Two primary fluid conduits run through these plants. **Xylem** carries water and soil materials dissolved in water through the plant, and **phloem** carries the products of photosynthesis and plant hormones.

### Materials
on side counter
chart of fern life cycle
chart of vascular seedless plants
fern specimen(s), including specimen with sori
dissecting probe
plain microscope slides
coverslips
dropper bottle with water

on your lab bench
compound light microscope

on instructor's bench
used slide container

### Procedure
STEP 1. Visit the side counter to observe the live specimens and charts of the seedless vascular plants, and answer the following questions.

6. What are some common plants that are in this group?

*Fern are common plant in their group.*

7. What is the general size and height of the seedless vascular plants compared to the non-vascular plants?

*They are taller plants*

STEP 2. Look on the underside of a fern frond. The orange-brown spots are **sori**, collections of fern sporangia.

8. Based on your observations of the fern, what is the most conspicuous, or dominant, multicellular generation in seedless vascular plants?

Sporophyte - largest produces spores

STEP 3. Prepare a slide of the fern sporangia by using a dissecting probe to scrape off the material from a sorus onto a slide. *You do not need to remove the leaf from the specimen!* Add a drop of water and a coverslip. Observe the slide on the compound light microscope at your bench.

9. DRAW the fern sorus.

10. What is the purpose of a spore?

It is used for reproduction.

STEP 4. Dispose of the slide in the used slide container on the instructor's bench.

## I. C. Tracheophytes/ vascular seed plants (gymnosperms and angiosperms)

Tracheophytes also include **vascular seed** plants. Seed plants started to outnumber other plants during the Mesozoic Era, which began about 250 million years ago, when conditions on Earth became warmer and drier. In the drier climate, new adaptations for growth and reproduction were naturally selected. Seeds are a package that contains not only the embryo, but also a food source and an outer protective coat. Due to the success of this reproductive strategy, most plants today are seed plants.

There are two major groups of plants that produce seeds. Most **gymnosperms** produce both pollen and seeds on **cones**, relying on wind for both **pollination** (the transfer of pollen from the male to the female structures) and seed dispersal. **Angiosperms** are flowering plants, often using insects or other animals for pollination. Angiosperms evolved more recently, and their ovules are located inside a modified leaf called an **ovary**; when the ovule becomes a seed, the ovary matures into a **fruit**. Gymnosperm seeds are called "naked" seeds by contrast.

**Materials**

on side counter

chart of the life cycle of a gymnosperm
chart of the life cycle of an angiosperm
chart(s) of vascular seed plant diversity
specimen(s) of vascular seed plants as available
Riker mount display of hardwood and softwood
vial with male pinecones and pine pollen
paintbrush
plain microscope slides
coverslips
dropper bottle with water

on your lab bench

prepared slides of pinecones, male and female
compound light microscope

on instructor's bench

used slide container

**Procedure**

STEP 1. Visit the side counter to observe the live specimens and charts of the vascular seed plants, and answer the following questions.

11. List examples of plants in this group.

*Pine cone, apple tree (Pine tree)*

12. What is the relative size of plants in this group compared to the other plant groups you have seen?

*Varies and larger - Really Big! large*

STEP 2. Observe the hardwood/softwood comparison mount on the side counter. Hardwoods come from angiosperms and softwoods come from gymnosperms.

13. How does hardwood differ from softwood? What advantage is there to hardwood floors over softwood floors?

*hard wood and softwood are differ from durability,*

STEP 3. Use your compound light microscope to locate the ovule and pollen in the prepared slides of pinecones on your microscope.

14. How do the sizes of the ovule and pollen compare?

*Pollen is small, ovule is large.*

STEP 4. At the side counter, prepare a slide of the pine pollen by using a paintbrush to get the pollen (yellow dust) from the male pinecone. Add a drop of water and a coverslip. Observe the pollen using the compound light microscope at your bench.

15. DRAW the structure of pine pollen here. How does its structure help with wind dispersal?

*to ~~area~~ be able to be carried by the wind.*

STEP 5. Dispose of the pine pollen slide in the used slide container on the instructor's bench.

## II. PLANT FORM AND ADAPTATIONS

With the advent of vascular tissue, plant structures were naturally selected that improved their function. The below-ground portion of the plant is called the **root**. The root absorbs water and essential minerals from the soil. The above-ground portion of the plant is called the **shoot**. Shoots include stems, leaves, and flowers, so the shoot functions in photosynthesis and sexual reproduction. Refer to Figure 13.2 on the next page showing the parts of the flowering plant.

Found within both the shoot and root are the two general types of vascular tissue that makes up the tube systems in plants. **Xylem** is vascular tissue that at maturity consists of hollow tubes made from the remnant of thick cell walls. Water is transported through the xylem by the process called **transpiration**. In the tubes of the xylem, the water column is continuous, so that when water molecules at the top of the plant evaporate from the leaves, water molecules will be pulled upward from the roots. How does this happen? As you recall, an important property of water is cohesion, i.e., water sticks to itself. Water also exhibits adhesion, sticking to the walls of the xylem.

The other tube system in plants is made of **phloem** tissue. Phloem includes large sieve-tube members and companion cells. Phloem is still living at maturity, and is not hollow. The companion cells actively transport the sugars produced by photosynthesis into the sieve-tube members, and water follows after the sugar, pushing the fluid through the phloem. Any plant tissue needing sugar will take it up from the phloem. This process is called **translocation**.

In the following activities you will learn about specific adaptations naturally selected in flowering plants.

**Figure 13.2 A flowering plant**

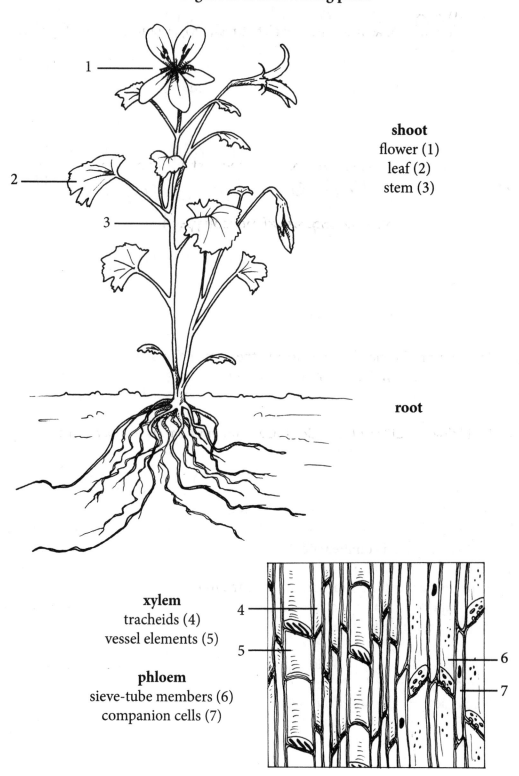

**shoot**
flower (1)
leaf (2)
stem (3)

**root**

**xylem**
tracheids (4)
vessel elements (5)

**phloem**
sieve-tube members (6)
companion cells (7)

**II. A. Roots**

**Materials**

on side counter
root model
chart of root adaptations: aerial, buttress, prop, storage, pneumatophores

on your lab bench
prepared slide of root nodules with *Rhizobium* sp.
prepared slide of root with mycorrhizae

**Procedure**
STEP 1. Go to the side counter to see the chart of root adaptations for different environmental conditions.

16.  Propose a reason for the pneumatophore root type.

air out of the water

STEP 2. Continue on the side counter to see the root model and locate the two fluid transport systems, the **xylem** and the **phloem**. Note that xylem and phloem tissue is bundled together.

17.  Fluid flows in different directions in a plant in xylem and phloem. In the xylem, what direction does fluid move through the plant, up or down?

It goes up the xylem.

STEP 3. Locate the root hairs on the model.

18.  How do root hairs assist the function of the root?

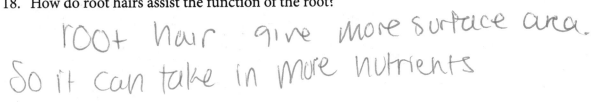
root hair give more surface area.
So it can take in more nutrients

**Symbiosis** is a term used to describe two organisms living together as one unit. When both benefit from the relationship, it is considered a mutualistic symbiosis. **Mycorrhizae** are a mutualistic symbiosis that occurs between most vascular plants and fungi. Another symbiosis is seen in some flowering plants with special root nodules that harbor *Rhizobium* sp. bacteria. The bacteria stimulate nodule growth in the plant root where the bacteria will transform atmospheric nitrogen into ammonia, which makes the nitrogen more accessible to the plant.

STEP 4. Return to your lab bench to use the compound light microscope to observe the prepared slide of mycorrhizae. The thread-like structures around the root are the fungal threads called **hyphae**.

    19.  Propose an explanation for the development of mycorrhizae symbioses.

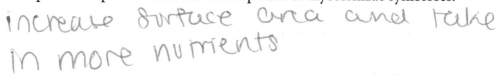

increase surface area and take in more nutrients

STEP 5. Observe the root nodules induced by *Rhizobium* sp. Most plant fertilizers include the key elements, nitrogen, potassium, and phosphorus.

    20.  How are plants with root nodules beneficial to a farmer?

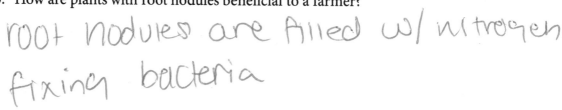

root nodules are filled w/ nitrogen fixing bacteria

The shoot of a flowering plant includes stems, leaves, and flowers (in season). Stems support the leaves and transport materials, and may photosynthesize. Leaves are the primary photosynthetic organs, and flowers are used in sexual reproduction.

## II. B. Shoots/ stems and leaves

Flowering plants that complete their life cycle in one year are called annuals, and plants that live more than one year are perennials. Perennials increase the girth of their stems by adding additional layers of vascular tissue.

**Materials**

on side counter

model of plant stem
Riker mount of basic leaf shapes
display of various plants with different leaf modifications
Somso deciduous leaf section model
*Kalanchoe* plant
plain microscope slides
coverslips
dropper bottle with water

on your lab bench

prepared slide, *Tilia* sp., 3-year old stem
prepared slide, ficus leaf cs
compound light microscope

on instructor's bench

used slide container

**Procedure**

STEP 1. Return to the side counter to see the model of a plant stem. The vascular tissue conduits (xylem and phloem) run continuously throughout the plant from the tip of the shoot to the tip of the root.

21.  How can there be a continuous flow of fluid between cells when plants have cell walls? *plasma stomata*

22.  In addition to sometimes photosynthesizing, how does the stem help the leaves with photosynthesis? *The stem is closer to the sun.*

STEP 2. Refer to Figure 13.3 below as you observe the prepared microscope slide of a three-year old *Tilia* sp. trunk with your compound light microscope. The xylem **growth rings** (7) are in the inner section of the trunk. The size of the annual xylem ring is a reflection of growing conditions: better conditions lead to thicker rings. The **phloem** (3) grows outside of the xylem. There is a very thin layer of **meristem** (stem cell growth tissue), called **vascular cambium** (5), located between the xylem and the phloem. The vascular cambium makes both new **xylem** (6) inward and new phloem outward. Outside of the phloem is another type of meristem tissue, the **cork cambium** (2), that makes a protective layer, the **cork** (1). The phloem, cork cambium, and cork make up the **bark** (4).

**Figure 13.3 Cross section of a tree trunk**

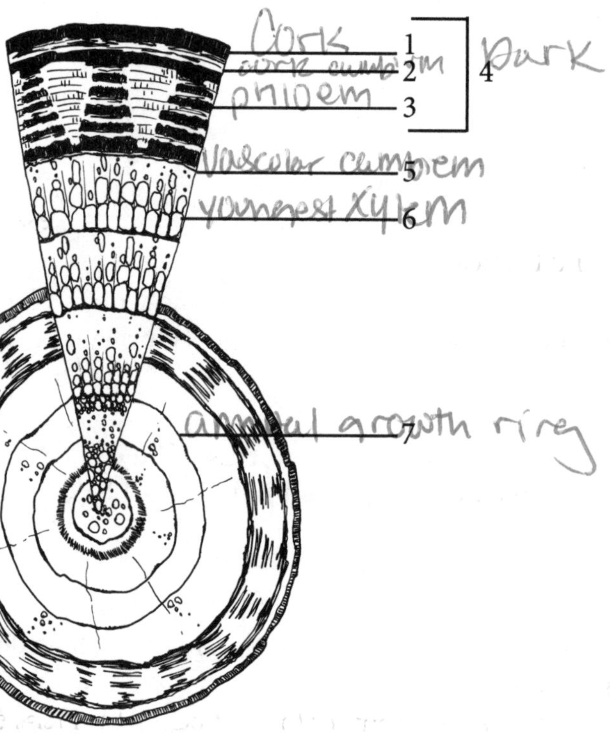

(1) cork
(2) cork cambium
(3) phloem
(4) bark

(5) vascular cambium
(6) youngest xylem
(7) annual growth ring

Both xylem sap and phloem sap transport fluid through the tree. The old xylem tissue has sturdy secondary cell walls and make up what we call **wood**. The oldest wood is in the center of the trunk and sometimes loses it ability to transport water when small pockets of air stop the flow of water molecules. The xylem in the center of a tree is referred to as **heartwood**, and the xylem further out is **sapwood**.

23. What happens when you remove the bark on a tree trunk?

It dies - losses nutrients

24. What materials flow through the xylem sap?

Water and nutrients.

STEP 3. Go to the side counter to look at the various leaf shapes of different plants on display.

25. If leaves function to maximize photosynthesis, why is there so much variety in leaf structure?

genetic diversity - adapt to diffrent enviroments

26. Match the leaf type with its habitat; select from desert, temperate dry, temperate wet, and tropical wet. Explain the reasoning behind your choices.

specimen A    - cactus - dessert

specimen B    - temp. dry

specimen C    temp. wet

specimen D    temp. wet

specimen E    temp. dry

STEP 4. Continue on the side counter to the model of a cross section of a leaf.

27. What are all the green structures within the cells in the middle of the leaf?

chloroplasts.

STEP 5. Locate holes in the epidermis (surface tissue) on the leaf model. These holes are called **stomata**.

28. Which of the three requirements for photosynthesis enters the leaves through the stomata?

$CO_2$

29.   What molecules could leave the plant through the stomata?

$CO_2$

STEP 6. Observe the prepared microscope slide of the ficus leaf using a compound light microscope.

30.   LABEL the following structures on Figure 13.4, cross section of a leaf: the epidermis, palisade mesophyll, spongy mesophyll, vascular bundle, and stomata. Charts and the model of the leaf are available on the side counter for your reference.

**Figure 13.4 Cross section of a leaf**

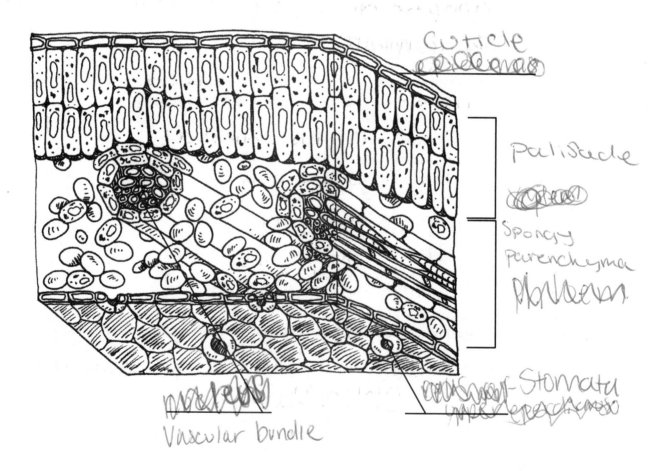

STEP 7. On the side counter you will find a *Kalanchoe* plant. Break off a leaf, and fold it down in half, careful not to break the very bottom layer, which is the epidermis. Peel off the lower epidermis, and place on a plain microscope slide with a drop of water. Cover with a coverslip, and observe under the compound light microscope.

31.  DRAW the surface of the leaf, labeling the openings, the stomata.

32.  Have your instructor verify your labels and drawing and initial your lab book here. _____

## II. C. Shoots/ flowers, seeds, fruit

The **sporophyte** is the dominant generation in angiosperm plants. Both types of gametophytes grow on the sporophyte plant. Flowers are the reproductive organs that produce the gametophytes. The female gametophyte is inside the ovule and the male gametophyte is inside the pollen. Flowers are comprised of **whorls** (concentric layers of specialized leaves). Please see Figure 13.5 on the next page. The innermost whorl is the ovule-producing **carpel** (1). The carpel has three components: the stigma (2), the syle (3), and the ovary (4). The next whorl is the pollen-producing **stamen** (5). The stamen has two components: the anther (6) and the filament (7) These gamete-producing parts of the flower are surrounded by whorls designed to attract pollinators, the **petals** (8) and the **sepals** (9).

### Materials

on side counter

    chart of carnivorous plant flowers
    flower
    paintbrush
    plain microscope slides
    coverslips
    chart with pollinators of various flowers
    bean seeds, soaking in water
    charts with fleshy and dry fruits
    dropper bottle with water
    dissecting microscope

on your lab bench

    compound light microscope

on instructor's bench

    used slide container

**Procedure**

STEP 1. Go to the side counter to pick up a flower and take it to your lab bench. Set up a dissecting microscope. While looking through the dissecting microscope, carefully separate each flower whorl. Match the parts of your specimen to Figure 13.5 below. *Keep your flower for use in further study and questions.*

**Figure 13.5 A flower**

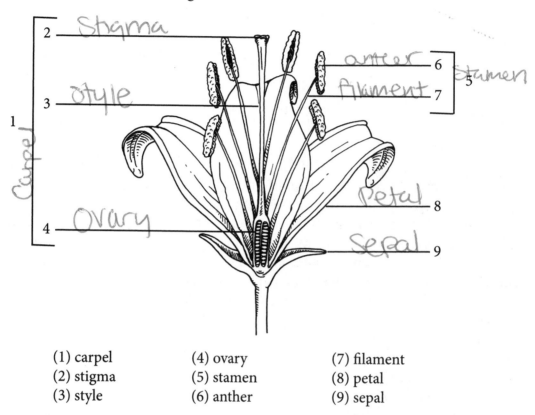

| | | |
|---|---|---|
| (1) carpel | (4) ovary | (7) filament |
| (2) stigma | (5) stamen | (8) petal |
| (3) style | (6) anther | (9) sepal |

33. Which part produces the pollen?

STEP 2. At the side counter, prepare a pollen slide by brushing a small amount of pollen from a flower onto a plain microscope slide, adding a drop of water and a coverslip.

STEP 3. Return to your lab bench to look at the pollen under the compound light microscope.

34. DRAW the flower pollen.

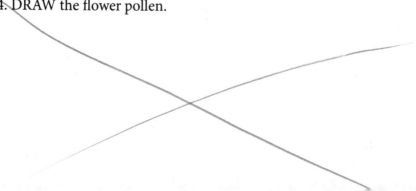

**Pollen** does not require water for sperm transfer but rather relies on wind or animals to carry the sperm to the female part of the plant. Flowering plants have competed for millions of years to get pollinators to spread their genetic material. Genetic diversity increases when pollen is carried to a different plant.

A wide variety of animal pollinators have been enlisted by plants, including insects, birds, and mammals. Some flowers provide nectar, a sugary syrup. Animals eat the nectar or pollen. The wide variety of flower shapes and smells are the result of natural selection by animals for their preferred flowers.

STEP 4. Look at the pollinator chart displayed on the side counter.

35. Identify three insect pollinators.

*hummingbird    beetle*
*butterflies    bumblebee*
*bees    moth*

36. Identify three non-insect animal pollinators.

*Birds, bat, lizards*

37. Identify a flower that is pollinated by each of the following animals.

bat    *Kapok tree*
bumblebee    *eggplant*
beetle    *magnolias*
lizard    *Flax*
lemur    *guava*
hummingbird    *tubular blossoms*

STEP 5. Return to your lab bench to revisit your flower dissection. Inside the ovary are the ovules. Make a horizontal cut through the middle of the ovary, and look for the ovules under the dissecting microscope. Ovules are located in small chambers called **locules**.

38. How many locules are there in the flower ovary?

*21 locules*

The ovules enclose the female egg-producing gametophyte. Once the egg is fertilized, the ovule becomes a **seed**. The angiosperm seed is more than just the new generation; it contains the embryo, a food source, and a protective coat. Tissue surrounding the embryo develops from other cells fertilized by a second sperm cell. Angiosperms, therefore, have double fertilization. As the embryo develops, hormones are released that put it into stasis. The outer skin, or integument, of the ovule dries and hardens to become the seed coat. The seed remains **dormant** until the proper conditions are met. Soaking in water releases the inhibitory hormones, and the seed can germinate. Some seeds more than a 1000 years old have germinated when planted and watered!

STEP 6. Go to the side counter and get a bean seed that has been soaking in water and take it to your lab bench for dissection under the dissecting scope.

39. LABEL the embryo, food source, and seed coat of the bean on Figure 13.6 below.

**Figure 13.6 A bean**

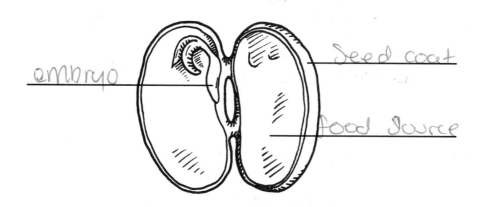

The ovule develops inside the ovary of the flower. When the egg is fertilized, so that the ovule becomes a seed, the ovary is said to mature into a **fruit**. Like flowers, fruits have evolved to attract animals. Animals move about, and when they eat a fruit, they carry the seeds away from the parent plant. This greatly increases the dispersal of seeds. Fruits can be fleshy, like a tomato or orange, or dry, like a peanut.

STEP 7. Go to the side counter to observe the various types of fleshy and dry fruits.

40. Identify one fleshy and one dry fruit here.

Fleshy: grapes

dry fruit - legumes , nut

41. Does the embryo get nourishment from the fruit? Explain your answer.

*no it has its own source*

STEP 8. Observe the chart of carnivorous plants on the side counter. These plants attract and trap animals like insects, worms, and spiders and secrete enzymes to chemically digest them for absorption.

42. Many of these carnivorous plants are located in lush, tropical rainforests or bogs. Can you propose a reason for this?

*They do not have enough nutrients in the soil.*

43. Are the carnivorous plants on display angiosperms or gymnosperms? What is your evidence?

*angiosperms - flowering*

## II. D. Monocots and Dicots

The angiosperms are currently grouped into one plant phylum, Anthophyta. Two major groups in the phylum Anthophyta are the monocots and dicots. These groups are named after their seed structure, but other structures differ as well. For instance, monocots generally have shallow, branching, and fibrous roots, while dicots tend to have deep taproots.

### Materials
on the side counter
      charts of monocots and dicots
      specimen of grass in Erlenmeyer flask
      Riker mount monocot vs. dicot display
      chart showing floral diversity

on your lab bench
      prepared slide of monocot root
      prepared slide of dicot root
      compound light microscope

### Procedure
STEP 1. On the side counter is a display comparing the seedlings, leaves, stems, and flowers of monocots and dicots. The leaves contain vascular bundles of xylem and phloem that look like, and are called **veins**. Flower whorls are found in distinct sets of numbers in the two groups.

44. How are the veins on a monocot arranged differently than on a dicot?

45. Monocots have flower whorls in groups of three, while dicots have flower whorls in groups of four or five. Is the sample flower you dissected a monocot or a dicot?

STEP 2. At your lab bench, use the compound light microscope to look at the prepared slides of the monocot and dicot roots. Use the chart comparing the roots of monocots and dicots on the side counter as a reference.

46. The arrangements of vascular bundles in the root differ between monocots and dicots. Explain how.

STEP 3. On the side counter there is a grass specimen on display. Describe the roots of grasses. Do you think they are monocots or dicots? Explain your answer.

47. Very tall palm trees can be successfully transplanted but similarly sized oak trees cannot be so easily moved. Explain why.

STEP 4. At the side counter look at the chart showing floral diversity.

48. Idenitfy one flowering plant that is a monocot and one that is a dicot. Explain why you selected those examples.

**SUMMARY QUESTION**

Describe the major structural adaptations found in land plants and explain how they enabled plant numbers to expand dramatically on dry land. One member of your group may be asked to share this with the class during discussion.

**POST-LAB QUESTIONS**                          **Name** _____

1.  Why were seeds an important advancement for plants in the Mesozoic Era?

2.  Why do you add fertilizer for a plant to the soil, and not just spray it on the leaves?

3.  How do the structures of pine pollen and flower pollen differ? Explain why the differences matter.

4.  The comet orchid of Madagascar has a 25-30 cm long nectar tube. Only a moth with a very long proboscis can reach inside. Explain an advantage and a disadvantage for the flower and the moth being this highly specialized.

5.  How many meters long is Madagascar comet orchid nectar tube?

6.  How do animals, fungi, and bacteria help plants thrive?

*Questions continue on the next page.*

7.  Identify the numbered structures.

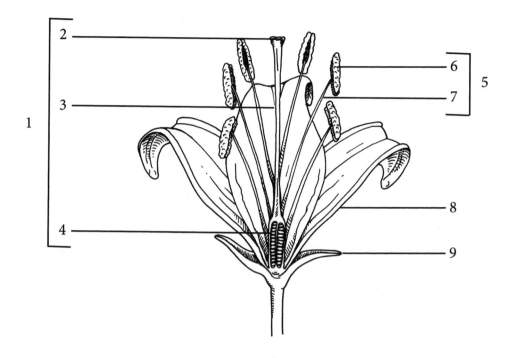

1. _____

2. _____

3. _____

4. _____

5. _____

6. _____

7. _____

8. _____

9. _____

# FUNGI

What is a fungus? What is the role of fungi on the Earth? How does fungal anatomy help them perform their role? These questions will form the framework for your activities in today's lab.

What is a fungus? The kingdom Fungi is in the domain Eukarya. The closest kingdom related to Fungi is Animalia. Fungi are found everywhere, in the soil, water, and air. Some fungi are unicellular and some are multicellular. The largest organism known on Earth is a pathogenic honey mushroom spreading from tree root to tree root in Oregon about ten square kilometers in size. Members of this kingdom are heterotrophic absorbers, getting their nutrition from other organic material. Fungi have cell walls that are made of chitin, unlike the cell walls of plants that are made of cellulose. Chitin is a material also found in the exoskeleton of arthropods. Fungi use glycogen as an energy storage molecule, like animals, not starch like plants.

What is the role of fungi on the Earth? Fungi secrete exoenzymes to break down organic material outside of their bodies before absorbing the nutrients. Fungi include **parasites** that get their nutrition from living hosts, and **saprobes** that feed on dead organic matter. Fungi can decompose cellulose, keratin, chitin, and lignin. Cellulose and lignin are found in plants, and chitin and keratin are found in animals. Fungi also form important symbioses with members of other kingdoms. For example, in the last lab you studied the mycorrhizal associations with vascular plants. Fungi also help small green algae and cyanobacteria colonize harsh dry habitats as part of symbioses called **lichens**. For people, fungi are economically important. The most economically important fungus is yeast, used for baking and brewing. We eat fungi, use them for medicine (e.g. penicillin, taxol), and industry (e.g. as a source of chemicals). Fungi are also used for scientific research to understand eukaryotes.

How does fungal anatomy help them perform their role? Fungi need to spread out to get the largest surface area to contact the organic material that provides them with energy. Fungi are made of filamentous threads, called **hyphae**. The entire body of a fungus is called the **mycelium**.

**PRE-LAB QUESTIONS**                    **Name** _____

1. How are plants and fungi alike and how are they different?



2. How are animals and fungi alike and how are they different?

STUDENT LEARNING OUTCOMES

Upon completion of this lab, you will be able to do the following:

I. describe the diversity of fungi,
II. discuss the life cycle of fungi and fungal anatomy, and
III. understand the role of fungi in ecosystems.

## I. THE DIVERSITY OF FUNGI

### Materials
on side counter
chart of Fungi phyla
chart of mushroom diversity

### Procedure
Go to the side counter to see the diversity of fungi.

1.  What is the common word root found in the names of the five phyla of fungi?

2.  Identify a phylum that includes fungi that you eat.

3.  What colors, shapes, and sizes do mushrooms have?

4.  Is it safe to eat any mushroom you find in the woods or in your yard? Explain your answer.

## II. THE LIFE CYCLE OF FUNGI AND FUNGAL ANATOMY

### Materials
on side counter
chart of Fungi phyla
chart of mushroom diversity
model of mushroom
dissecting microscope
used slide container

on your lab bench
> mushroom for dissection
> Petri dish
> paring knife
> forceps
> dropper bottle with water
> microscope slides
> coverslips
> compound light microscope

Most fungi are haploid most of their lives, reproducing asexually by releasing haploid spores of the same genotype. Fungi can also reproduce sexually. An individual fungus is not considered either male or female because fungi do not produce eggs and sperm like animals. Individuals with a different genotype are categorized as different **mating types**.

To reproduce sexually, the cytoplasm of cells from two mating types merge together. However, the nuclei of the mating fungi do not fuse together immediately. Because their cytoplasm fuses but their nuclei stay separate for a time, the tissue is called **heterokaryotic**. Fungi are classified into phyla by the sexual reproductive structure that develops following the cytoplasmic fusion. The nuclei from the two mating types fuse in the sexual reproductive structures. When the nuclei fuse, the resulting zygote almost immediately undergoes meiosis to form haploid spores.

The mushrooms that you eat are actually the sexual reproductive structures of the fungus. The gills underneath the cap have structures called **basidia**. The basidium is the location of the fusion of the nuclei of two mating types. Meiosis follows almost immediately after fusion of the two nuclei. The basidia release the sexually produced haploid spores that will grow into the next generation. The mating types are distinguished by a plus (+) or minus (–) on Figure 14.1 on the next page.

5. What is the name of the fungal phylum with mushrooms? How did that phylum get its name?

6. Why is the mushroom cap above ground?

STEP 1. Review the life cycle of a mushroom on the charts and in Figure 14.1.

7. LABEL the following structures in Figure 14.1: stipe, cap, gills, basidium, spore.

**Figure 14.1 The life cycle of a mushroom**

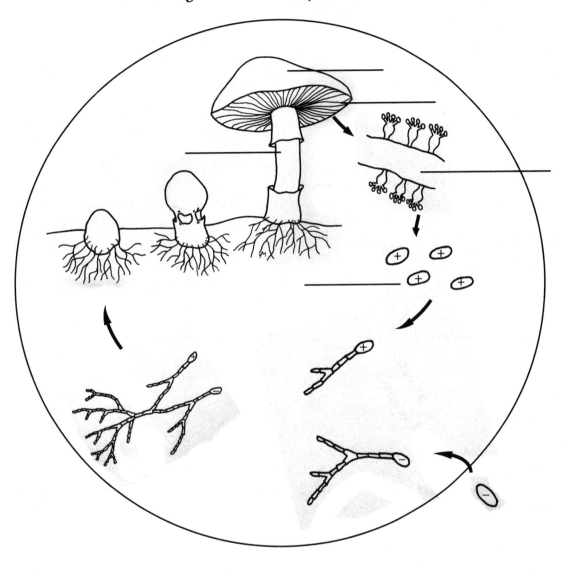

STEP 2. View the model of the mushroom.

8. Identify the basidia by the number on the model. _____

9. What cellular process will occur on the gills after the fusion of the nuclei?


STEP 3. Return to your lab bench and place the mushroom on the Petri dish.

STEP 4. Set up a dissecting microscope. Using the paring knife, cut the cap off the mushroom, and then cut the stalk lengthwise. The thin, hairlike filaments you will see where you split the stem are the hyphae.

10. Describe the hyphal structures of the stalk.

11. What is the function of the fungal hyphae?

STEP 5. Using the dissecting micoscope, look at the underside of the cap to study the gills. Each gill is lined with thousands of small structures called basidia.  Using your forceps, gently remove one gill from the cap. Place the gill on a microscope slide and add a drop of water and a coverslip to prepare a wet mount. Place the slide on the compound light microscope and examine the edge of the gill that was not attached to the mushroom under low power. Switch the microscope to high power and look at the finger-like projections. These are the basidia.  If your mushroom is mature the basidia may have spores attached to them.

12. Fungi reproduce by spores. How are spores structurally different from seeds?

13. How are spores dispersed?

STEP 6. Discard the wet mount slide you prepared into the used slide container on the side counter and throw out the dissected mushroom in the trash.

## III. THE ROLE OF FUNGI IN ECOSYSTEMS

### Materials
on side counter
> photo of mushroom on fallen tree
> demonstration of bread mold, *Rhyzopus* sp.
> lichen specimens: foliose, crustose, and fruticose
> demonstration slide of lichen
> display of various fungal associations with other kingdoms
> display chart of the economic uses of fungi
> model of snail
> algal specimen, photo and/or model

Often you will see mushrooms sprouting on fallen trees, as in the photograph on the side counter. However, their handiwork is seen even closer to home.

STEP 1. On the side counter, compare the model of the mushroom from the kingdom Fungi and the model of the snail from the kingdom Animalia.

14. What similarities and differences do you see between these two eukaryan specimens?

STEP 2. Compare the structures of algae on display with the fungi on display.

15. Fungi and algae get their energy in two very different ways. How can you determine this from the way they look?

STEP 3. Observe the demonstration of a bread mold on a dissecting microscope. The fungus has spread throughout the bread.

16. What are two ways the fungus spreads across the bread?

17. What important job is the bread mold fungus doing for the ecosystem?

Lichens are a symbiosis between a fungus and a photosynthetic partner, usually a green alga or a cyanobacterium. The photosynthetic partner provides carbohydrates and the fungus helps by absorbing water and minerals. Lichens covering rocks extend their thin hyphae into tiny cracks and break down the rock, releasing minerals for other organisms to use.

STEP 4. Observe the different types of lichens displayed on the side counter.

18. Match the group with its appearance.

crustose    _____     A. shrub-like, branching, fibrous

foliose     _____     B. leaf-like, flat

fruticose   _____     C. forms a crust on the surface

STEP 5. Examine the prepared slide of lichen on display on a compound light microscope.

19. Are the algal cells congregated to one side separate from the fungal hyphae or are they found within the fungal hyphae? Explain the value of this organization.

STEP 6. Study the many ways fungi interact with other kingdoms by looking at the display.

20. Identify at least three distinct ways people use fungi.

21. Identify two distinct ways fungi interact with members of other kingdoms. Indicate if the relationship is beneficial or harmful.

## SUMMARY QUESTION

What would happen if all the fungi disappeared from the earth? One member of your group may be asked to share this with the class during discussion.

# APPENDICES

# APPENDIX A

## THE METRIC SYSTEM

| Prefix name | Prefix Symbol | $10^n$ | Base Unit Equivalents | Common Name |
|---|---|---|---|---|
| yotta | Y | $10^{24}$ | 1000000000000000000000000 | Septillion |
| zetta | Z | $10^{21}$ | 1000000000000000000000 | Sextillion |
| exa | E | $10^{18}$ | 1000000000000000000 | Quintillion |
| peta | P | $10^{15}$ | 1000000000000000 | Quadrillion |
| tera | T | $10^{12}$ | 1000000000000 | Trillion |
| giga | G | $10^9$ | 1000000000 | Billion |
| mega | M | $10^6$ | 1000000 | Million |
| kilo | k | $10^3$ | 1000 | Thousand |
| hecto | h | $10^2$ | 100 | Hundred |
| deca | da | $10^1$ | 10 | Ten |
| **Base unit (m, L, g)** | | $10^0$ | 1 | **One** |
| deci | d | $10^{-1}$ | 0.1 | Tenth |
| centi | c | $10^{-2}$ | 0.01 | Hundredth |
| milli | m | $10^{-3}$ | 0.001 | Thousandth |
| micro | μ | $10^{-6}$ | 0.000001 | Millionth |
| nano | n | $10^{-9}$ | 0.000000001 | Billionth |
| pico | p | $10^{-12}$ | 0.000000000001 | Trillionth |
| femto | f | $10^{-15}$ | 0.000000000000001 | Quadrillionth |
| atto | a | $10^{-18}$ | 0.000000000000000001 | Quintillionth |
| zepto | z | $10^{-21}$ | 0.000000000000000000001 | Sextillionth |
| yocto | y | $10^{-24}$ | 0.000000000000000000000001 | Septillionth |

larger

smaller

# APPENDIX B

## CONVERSIONS BETWEEN UNITS OF MEASURE

### I. Metric to metric

Converting between units is a matter of moving the decimal point (each point moved will reflect a factor of 10) the correct direction and number of places. This is most easily determined by examining the exponents ($10^n$) and knowing which prefix is bigger or smaller. If converting from a larger unit to a smaller unit, the decimal point will move to the right, if moving from a smaller unit to a larger unit the decimal point will move to the left.

### Equivalence Statements, Metric/Metric

1 meter (m) = 1000 mm
1 m = 100 cm
1 m = 10 dm
1 cm = 10 mm
1 liter (L) = 1000 mL
1 kilogram (kg) = 1000 g
1 g = 1000 mg

### Examples

A. 17 terraballs equals how many megaballs?

Look at the table to determine that terra(T) = $10^{12}$ and mega(M) = $10^6$. This means we will move the decimal point 6 places (the difference between the exponents $10^{12}$–$10^6$=$10^6$). But which direction?

Because we are converting from a larger unit to a smaller unit, move the decimal point right 6 places, so: 17 Tballs = 17,000,000 Mballs.

B. 83,000,000 g equals how many kg?

Look at the table to determine that g ($10^0$) – kg($10^3$)=$10^{-3}$ tells us that we will be moving the decimal point three places and because we are converting from a smaller unit to a larger unit, the decimal point will move to the left (notice also that the exponent is *negative* 3), so: 83,000,000 g = 83,000 kg.

## II. Metric to standard/ standard to metric

Conversions between metric and standard units use equivalence statements comparing the two systems. Adapt the equivalence statement to a ratio, and then multiply it by the known value to convert your known value to the other unit. Be sure that you set up your problem so that the units cancel properly!

### Equivalence Statements, Metric/Standard

1 foot = 12 inches
1 inch = 2.54 cm
1 oz = 28.35 grams
1 kg = 2.2 lb. or 35.27 oz
1 ounce (oz) = 29.57 mL
1 quart (qt) = 946 mL or 32 oz or .946 L
To convert from °F to °C:  °C = (°F - 32)/1.8
To convert from °C to °F:  °F = (°C x 1.8)+ 32

### Example

The height of a man is 6 feet 2 inches.  How tall is he in centimeters (cm)?
Information given:
Height of man = 6 feet 2.0 inches
Equivalence statements:
1 foot = 12 inches
1 inch = 2.54 cm

Height of man in inches:
6 feet X 12 inches/1 foot = 72 inches, plus 2 inches
Total height of man, in inches = 74 inches

Height of man in cm:
74.0 inches X 2.54cm/1 inch = 188 cm

# CONVERSION PRACTICE PROBLEMS

**Name** _____

## Practice Conversions of Mass
Conversions between metric and standard units:

    1 oz = 28.35 grams
    1 kg = 2.2 lb. or 35.27 oz

   1.  If a man weighs 180 lbs, how many kilograms (kg) does he weigh?

   2.  How many kg of liquid are in an 18-oz can of soda?

## Practice Conversions of Volume
Equivalence statements between metric & standard units of volume:

    1 ounce (oz) = 29.57 mL
    1 quart (qt) = 946 mL or 32 oz or .946 L

   3.  How many oz are in a 500-mL can?

   4.  Which volume is larger, 1 liter or 1 quart?

## Practice Conversions of Temperature

Conversion between °F and °C is relatively easy, and is as follows

To convert from °F to °C:          °C= (°F - 32)/1.8
To convert from °C to°F           °F = (°C x 1.8)+ 32

5.  Which is warmer, 30°F or 30°C?

6.  Convert 50°F to degrees in Celsius.

## Practice Conversions of Length

7.  Determine your height in centimeters (cm) by measurement or conversion.  If you are converting from the English system, 1 inch = 2.54 cm.

# ADDITIONAL CONVERSION PRACTICE PROBLEMS

**Name** _____

1. 25.6 m = _____ cm

2. 83.0 cm = _____ km

3. 73.75 in = _____ m

4. 322,190 mm = _____ feet

5. ½ in = _____ μm

6. 1500 m = _____ yds

7. How many mL are there in 2.5 liters? _____

8. What is the volume in uL of an object that is 1.4mm by .5mm by .5mm?

9. How many grams are in 0.25 kg?

10. 6,700,000 mg is equal to how many g?

11. A person from Finland may experience wintertime temperatures around -30°C, what is this in °F?

# APPENDIX C

## THE COMPOUND LIGHT MICROSCOPE

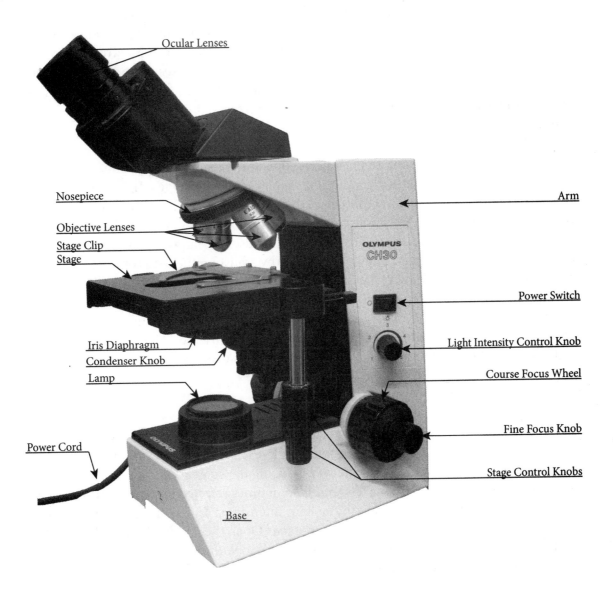

Ocular Lenses

Nosepiece

Objective Lenses

Stage Clip

Stage

Iris Diaphragm

Condenser Knob

Lamp

Power Cord

Base

Arm

Power Switch

Light Intensity Control Knob

Course Focus Wheel

Fine Focus Knob

Stage Control Knobs

# APPENDIX D

## USING THE COMPOUND LIGHT MICROSCOPE

The compound light microscope has multiple lenses to magnify an object. The lenses that will be next to your eyes are called the **ocular lenses**. The other lenses are located on a rotating nosepiece and will be close to the object, so they are called the **objective** lenses. The magnification factor for each lens is printed on the lens. Light passes through an object and is magnified by both lenses, so the *total* **magnification** is the product of the magnification factor of each lens. However, as the magnification increases, the **field of view** and **depth of field** decrease.

Objects for view in a compound light microscope are prepared in very thin sections and placed on a glass microscope slide. The slide is placed on the **stage**. The amount of light passing through an object can be controlled in several ways. The light-intensity knob controls the total amount of light shining on your field of view. Light passes from the lamp through a **condenser** to the object. The condenser focuses the light on your object. You will be able to maximize the resolution of your image by adjusting the focus of light by moving the condenser up and down with the condenser knob and opening the **iris diaphragm** lever found just beneath the stage. Adjusting the light in this manner will improve resolution and contrast. **Resolution** is the ability to distinguish between two points on the object; therefore, the greater the resolution, the more detail you can observe. **Contrast** distinguishes light and dark parts of the object.

Step by step instructions for optimum results:

1. Begin by placing the slide on the stage properly within the stage clips.
2. Ensure that the lowest magnification objective lens (4X) is in position directly above the stage. Move the stage all the way up using the coarse focus knob. This lens will provide the largest field of view, and is sometimes referred to as the scanning lens.
3. Turn the light on and start with the light intensity at 1. Use the condenser knob to move the condenser to just below the stage. Open the iris diaphragm all the way.
4. Place your hand on the coarse focus knob and look through the ocular lenses. Slowly lower the stage with the coarse focus knob until the object comes into view and in focus. You may increase the light intensity slowly until the object is well illuminated.
5. Adjust your eyepieces in the following manner. Close your left eye. While looking with your right eye through the right eyepiece, adjust the coarse, and then the fine focus to bring the specimen into focus. Then open your left eye, close your right eye, and look through the left eyepiece with your left eye. Adjust the diopter ring on the left eyepiece to focus the specimen. Change the inter-pupillary distance of the eyepieces until the left and right fields of view coincide.
6. The condenser and iris diaphragm are used to readjust the focus of light for the field of view at each magnification and light intensity. The iris diaphragm controls the

diameter of the light beam passing through the object, and is readjusted each time you change the objective lens. Start with the condenser just below the stage and the iris diaphragm all the way open. Slowly close the iris diaphragm until you get the best resolution. To further clarify your object, especially if it is thick, try lowering the condenser to help with the depth of field contrast.

7. Move the area of interest to the center of the field using the stage knobs.

8. If you need additional magnification, click the next higher objective lens into place. The lenses are parfocal, meaning they require little or no additional focusing when you switch lenses. If necessary, adjust the focus using the fine focus knob only; the coarse focus knob is only for use with the scanning lens. *Care must be taken not to raise or lower the stage too quickly when adjusting the microscope at higher magnifications to avoid damage to the lenses or the slides.* Readjust the iris diaphragm and condenser with each change in magnification.

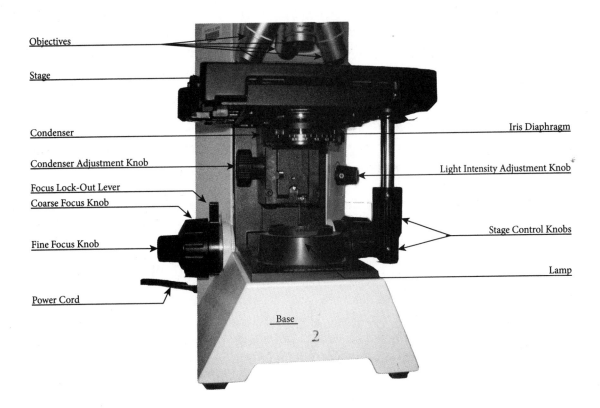

Objectives

Stage

Condenser

Condenser Adjustment Knob

Focus Lock-Out Lever

Coarse Focus Knob

Fine Focus Knob

Power Cord

Iris Diaphragm

Light Intensity Adjustment Knob

Stage Control Knobs

Lamp

Base

2

# APPENDIX E

## COLORS OF WAVELENGTHS IN THE VISIBLE SPECTRUM

| wavelength (nm) | color |
|:---:|:---:|
| 380-435 | violet |
| 435-500 | blue |
| 500-520 | cyan |
| 520-565 | green |
| 565-590 | yellow |
| 590-625 | orange |
| 625-740 | red |

# APPENDIX F

## FREQUENCY DATA AND HISTOGRAMS

A **histogram** is used to represent the frequency of specimens within specified intervals.

The table below shows the weight in grams of a sample of pinto beans.

### Weight of pinto beans

| bean | weight (g) | bean | weight (g) | bean | weight (g) |
|------|-----------|------|-----------|------|-----------|
| 1 | 1.1 | 15 | 1.3 | 29 | 2.3 |
| 2 | 1.2 | 16 | 1.2 | 30 | 1.5 |
| 3 | 1.6 | 17 | 1.9 | 31 | 0.9 |
| 4 | 1.2 | 18 | 1.8 | 32 | 1.7 |
| 5 | 1.4 | 19 | 1.2 | 33 | 1.9 |
| 6 | 1.1 | 20 | 0.8 | 34 | 2 |
| 7 | 1.8 | 21 | 0.6 | 35 | 1.4 |
| 8 | 1.7 | 22 | 1 | 36 | 1.3 |
| 9 | 1.7 | 23 | 1.1 | 37 | 1.7 |
| 10 | 1 | 24 | 1.3 | 38 | 1.1 |
| 11 | 1.1 | 25 | 0.7 | 39 | 1.2 |
| 12 | 1.4 | 26 | 2 | 40 | 0.9 |
| 13 | 1.5 | 27 | 2.1 | | |
| 14 | 1.6 | 28 | 1.2 | | |

The **range** of the data is the difference between the largest and smallest values.
Range = (largest value – smallest value) = (2.3g – 0.6g) = 1.7g

In this example, notice that every bean weight will fall between 2.3g and 0.6g and no two beans will differ in weight by more than 1.7g (the range).

To evaluate the distribution of beans throughout the range, the data is divided into groups called **intervals**. Usually 5 or 10 intervals are adequate. The interval size and can be found by dividing the range by the number of intervals you've chosen to use. We'll use 10 intervals for this example.

$$\text{Interval size} = \frac{\text{data range}}{\text{\# of intervals}} = \frac{1.7g}{10} = 0.17g$$

A **frequency table** is constructed to establish how many bean weights fall into each interval.

| interval | interval width (g) | # of beans |
|----------|--------------------|------------|
| 1 | 0.60-0.77 | 2 |
| 2 | 0.77-0.94 | 3 |
| 3 | 0.94-1.11 | 7 |
| 4 | 1.11-1.28 | 6 |
| 5 | 1.28-1.45 | 6 |
| 6 | 1.45-1.62 | 4 |
| 7 | 1.62-1.79 | 3 |
| 8 | 1.79-1.96 | 4 |
| 9 | 1.96-2.13 | 2 |
| 10 | 2.13-2.30 | 1 |

1. The first interval begins with the smallest bean weight (0.6g) and extends one **interval size** (0.17g) upwards. In other words, to get the upper limit of the first interval, add the interval size to the smallest bean weight:

0.60g + 0.17g = 0.77g
Interval 1 is 0.6g to 0.77g.

The second interval begins where the first one stops, so add the interval size to 0.77g.

0.77g + 0.17g = 0.94g
Interval 2 is 0.77g to 0.94 g.

Repeat this procedure for all ten intervals. The last interval should conclude with the weight of the heaviest bean (2.30g).

2. Use your data table to count of the number of beans in each interval. For example, a bean that weighs 0.7g would be in the first interval because it falls within the interval of 0.6g to 0.77g. Note: should a bean weight fall on the value dividing two intervals, include it in the upper interval.

Once you have your data sorted into a frequency table, it can be plotted for a **histogram** as follows:

1. The **independent variable** is the interval width, which is plotted on the x-axis. Frequency (the number in each variable) is the **dependent variable** and is plotted on the y-axis.
2. Divide the x and y axes into equal intervals and label the intervals as determined in the frequency table.
3. Label the axes with the name of the variable and the units of measure. It is better to label the y-axis with what is being counted rather than "frequency."
4. Draw a vertical bar for each frequency within an interval. If an interval has no data, leave that interval blank. Notice that the bars are touching each other.
5. Provide a meaningful title for the histogram.

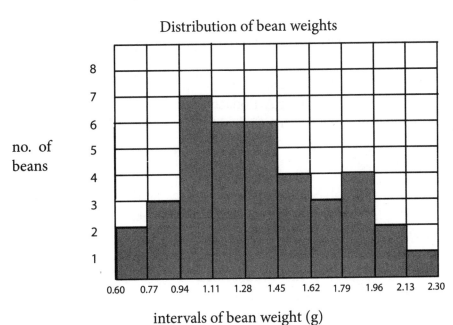

Distribution of bean weights

no. of beans

intervals of bean weight (g)

# APPENDIX G

## TAXONOMY AND CLASSIFICATION

### TAXONOMIC HIERARCHY OF THE WOLF, *Canis lupus*

domain Eukarya
    kingdom Animalia
        phylum Chordata
            class Mammalia
                order Carnivora
                    family Canidae
                        genus *Canis*
                            species *lupus*

### SELECTED CLASSES OF THE PHYLUM CHORDATA

phylum Chordata
    class Chondricthyes
    class Actinopterygii
    class Sarcopterygii
    class Amphibia
    class Reptilia
    class Aves
    class Mammalia

### SELECTED ORDERS OF THE CLASS MAMMALIA

class Mammalia
    order Artiodactyla
    order Carnivora
    order Cetacea
    order Chiroptera
    order Insectivora
    order Marsupialia
    order Monotremata
    order Pinnepedia
    order Primate
    order Proboscidea
    order Rodentia

# CLASSIFICATION OF SELECTED ANIMAL PHYLA

DOMAIN EUKARYA

  KINGDOM ANIMALIA

    PARAZOA (no true tissues)

      phylum Porifera

    EUMETAZOA (animals with true tissues)

      RADIATA (radial symmetry)

        phylum Cnidaria

      BILATERIA (bilateral symmetry)

        PROTOSTOMES

          SPIRALIA (animals that grow continuously in mass)

            phylum Platyhelminthes

            phylum Mollusca

            phylum Annelida

          ECDYSOZOA (animals that molt)

            phylum Nematoda

            phylum Arthropoda

        DEUTEROSTOMES

          phylum Echinodermata

          phylum Chordata

# CLASSIFICATION OF SELECTED PLANT PHYLA

DOMAIN EUKARYA

- KINGDOM PLANTAE

(BRYOPHYTES)

phylum Bryophyta

phylum Hepatophyta

(TRACHEOPHYTES)

(PTEROPHYTES)

phylum Pterophyta

phylum Lycophyta

(SEED PLANTS)

GYMNOSPERMS

phylum Coniferophyta

phylum Cycadophyta

phylum Ginkgophyta

phylum Gnetophyta

ANGIOSPERMS

phylum Anthophyta

# APPENDIX H

## PREPARING A SIMPLE GRAPH

Graphs are used by scientists to provide a quick visual summary of data. Graphs are usually easier to grasp than long lists of numbers found in tables. The graph uses the data from your experimental results.

### Procedure
STEP 1. Tabulate your experimental results. One column will contain the values from a variable that you manipulated. The variable that you manipulate is the independent variable. A second column contains the results of your experiment. Each number in the second column represents the result of the manipulation of your independent variable. These numbers depend on the value of the independent variable. The second column therefore contains your dependent variable. In the example below, time is the independent variable, and distance moved is the dependent variable.

| Time (minutes) | Distance moved (cm) |
|:---:|:---:|
| 0 | 0 |
| 15 | 10 |
| 30 | 25 |
| 45 | 50 |

STEP 2. On graph paper, label each axis with the variables and units used. The independent variable is plotted on the horizontal axis; the dependent variable is plotted on the vertical axis. The values on the axes should be based on the range of values of the data. Fill the graph paper; you may select more than one graph square to represent a unit.

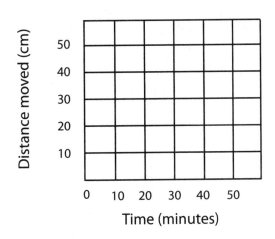

STEP 3. A scattergram is a graph representing the distribution of two variables. The values of each independent variable with its corresponding dependent variable represent a point on the graph. Place a mark on the graph where each independent value intersects with its dependent value.

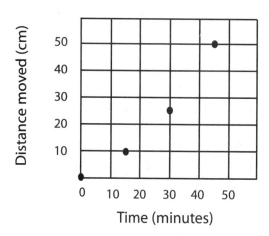

STEP 4. Title your graph with information to describe the relationship between the independent and dependent values.

The distance a liquid moved over time

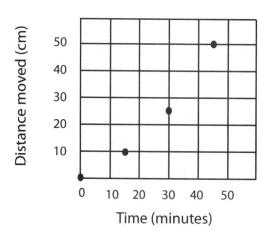